Dr James Douglas's Papers and Drawings in the Hunterian Collection, Glasgow University Library

A Handlist

Wellcome Unit for the History of Medicine
University of Glasgow
Publication No. 6
1994

Series Editor: Malcolm Nicolson

Previous Publications:

Wendy Alexander
First Ladies of Medicine 1987

Stephen Patterson
Finding Fife's Medical Records 1992

Robert Campbell Garry
Life in Physiology 1992

Alastair Tough
Medical Archives of Glasgow and Paisley 1993

Hamish Maxwell-Stewart, Alastair Tough, John Hope McColl and Johanna Geyer-Kordesch
Selecting Clinical Records for Long-Term Preservation
1993

Dr James Douglas's Papers and Drawings in the Hunterian Collection, Glasgow University Library

A Handlist

C Helen Brock

Wellcome Unit for the History of Medicine
University of Glasgow

C. Helen Brock is a zoologist and was formerly honorary research fellow in the Department of History of Science, Glasgow University. She became interested in James Douglas through his papers on comparative anatomy.

This publication has been made possible by the financial support of the Wellcome Trust. Grateful acknowledgement is made to the Royal Society for permission to reproduce passages from the Society's *Journal Book.*

Published by Wellcome Unit for the History of Medicine
5 University Gardens
University of Glasgow
Glasgow, G12 8QQ

ISBN 0 9511765 5 2

Print Layout by Malcolm Nicolson
Printed by Glasgow University Printing Department

Cover Illustration: Drawing of skull by F. Boitard for Douglas's unpublished 'Osteology', DF 3(78). Reproduced by kind permission of the Keeper of Special Collections, Glasgow University Library.

Preface

Dr James Douglas (1675-1742) MD, FRS, Douglas of the Pouch, Physician in Extraordinary to Queen Caroline, physician and man midwife, anatomist and teacher of anatomy, an outstanding comparative anatomist, botanist, grammarian, phoneticist and classical scholar, was described by Alexander Pope as "a physician of great learning and no less taste".[1] He was praised by Albrecht von Haller (1708-1777) as "erudite and clever, an extremely accurate dissector yet unassuming and most humane. An old man of experience [Haller] praises his benign intellect to the young".[2]

Yet Douglas has no place in present-day histories of eighteenth-century medicine. This may be because, as Haller lamented, "so few things from the great labours of this great man have come down to [later] generations". Douglas failed to publish his great Osteology, his treatises on human reproduction and the diseases of women, on hernias and aneurisms, and only one of the projected manuals for dissecting all parts of the body. But he did publish eleven books that made important contributions to anatomy, surgery, botany and bibliography, and eleven of his papers to the Royal Society were published in the *Philosophical Transactions.*

William Hunter (1718-1783) who for a time was Douglas's anatomy assistant, came to possess all Douglas's papers and drawings and they are now in the Hunterian Library, Glasgow University. In them is contained a record of Douglas's wide-ranging interests. There are extensive working papers on numerous medical subjects, his incomplete treatises, texts of papers given to the Royal Society but not published in the *Philosophical Transactions,* lecture notes, and notes of lectures, and an extensive collection of case histories demonstrating very fully the practice of medicine in the first half of the eighteenth century. There is also a large collection of papers relating to his interests outside medicine.

Douglas's papers show how much William Hunter's work was based on Douglas's interests and investigations: on hernias, aneurisms, the cellular membrane (connective tissue), comparative anatomy, even the lymphatics, on pathological anatomy and most importantly, Douglas's work on the anatomy and physiology of reproduction. Hunter's interest in medical history may have stemmed from Douglas's historical approach to medical subjects. Douglas, before Hunter, was convinced of the advantages to the student of dissecting for themselves. Lacking available human cadavers he encouraged them to dissect dogs and compare their anatomy with that of man, thereby teaching comparative anatomy as well. John Hunter (1728-1793), while he worked with his brother, had access to the Douglas papers and indeed purloined some of them, and may have found in them his enthusiasm for comparative anatomy.

A consideration of Douglas's papers together with his publications should gain him a place in the history of eighteenth-century medicine, comparative anatomy and botany. There have already been modern assessments of Douglas as grammarian and phonetist.[3]

Helen Brock
Cambridge, 1993

---

1 Alexander Pope *The Dunciad*, (1742) Bk IV, ii, 391-4, and footnote.

2 *Vir eruditus & solers, diligentissimus incisor, modestus idem vir & humanissimus, cujus benignum animum juventis expertus senex laudo. Vidi certe numerosissimas sceletos, multas etiam cum suis ligamentis in aqua jacentes, ut articulorum mobilitas sibi constaret: ossa etiam varie dissecta, ut interiora paterent. Verum magnum, quod parabat & promiserat, de ossibus opus interiit, & pauca sunt omnino, quae de maximis summi viri laboribus ad posteros pervenerunt.* Albrecht Haller *Bibliotheca Anatomica,* (1777) vol II, p 31, Tiguri.

3 Ian Michael *English Grammatical Categories*, (1970) London; Börge Holmberg *James Douglas on English Pronunciation circa 1740,* (1956) Lund.

Contents

Introduction

James Douglas, who has given his name to a fold in the peritoneal lining of the abdomen known as the Pouch of Douglas, was the second son of William and Joan Douglas of Baads, twelve miles west of Edinburgh. The exact date of his birth is not known but he was baptised 21 March 1675. Nothing is known of his schooling and very little about his higher education. A James Douglas, who might have been from Baads, graduated MA in 1694 at Edinburgh University and a James Douglas, that same year, was granted permission to go to Harwich and embark within fourteen days for Holland, (State Papers). This may have been James Douglas of Baads on his way to Utrecht, for he was there in 1698, undoubtedly studying medicine, for he made a catalogue of his library that year, consisting mainly of medical books. Surviving notes he took of lectures suggest that he also may have studied in Paris before he graduated MD at Rheims in 1699. Returning to Britain, he settled in London about 1700, and became assistant to Dr. Paul Chamberlen of the obstetric forceps family.

Except for notes on cases he attended, the first public appearance he made was reviewing a book at the Royal Society on 5 May 1705, a review afterwards published in the *Philosophical Transactions*. The next year he was elected to a Fellowship. He was the first of four Douglas brothers to achieve that distinction. His older brother Walter was elected in 1711 on appointment as Chief Governor and Vice Admiral of the Leeward Islands. It was a courtesy election for he had no scientific pretensions. In 1715 he was recalled, accused of maladministration, fined £500 and imprisoned for five years. John Douglas, some years younger than James, was a surgeon and served for some years as Surgeon General in the Leeward Islands but was back in London in 1717 and became a successful practitioner and lecturer in surgery. He was elected a Fellow in 1725 after he had developed the supra-pubic lithotomy operation. George, the youngest of the family, was born in 1693 and matriculated at Glasgow University in 1713 but graduated MD at Rheims in 1727. For some years he worked with James and acted as his amanuensis.

He published a translation of Winslow's *Exposition Anatomique* in 1732; dedicating the first volume to James to whom he owed all he knew "not only of the science but of the style of anatomy". He was elected a Fellow of the Royal Society in that year. Leaving James to go to St Christopher, he died there in 1736.

James Douglas was married twice. Who his first wife was is not known. There may have been one daughter of this first marriage. Secondly he married Martha Wilkes, aunt to John Wilkes, the politician. By her he had three children, Israel James, Martha Jane (1716-1744) and William George (c. 1725-1755). Israel James became an apothecary. He suffered, probably, from tuberculosis and must have died before 1752 for he was not mentioned in the will of his mother who died that year.

From 1705 onwards there is enough documentation to demonstrate James Douglas's interests and activities. He was a practising physician and man-midwife and became Physician in Extraordinary to Queen Caroline, anatomist and teacher of anatomy, zoologist, botanist, grammarian, phoneticist and classical scholar. While some of this information comes from records held by the Royal Society and the British Library, from newspapers and published diaries and contemporary histories, by far the richest source of information is the large collection of papers and drawings in the Hunterian Library, Glasgow University.

How these came into the possession of William Hunter is not known. In 1741 Hunter became anatomical assistant to James Douglas and tutor to his son, William George who was studying medicine. When James Douglas died in 1742 Hunter continued to live with the Douglas's, and after taking William George to Paris in 1743 to attend anatomy lectures, returned to the Douglas household in 1744 and lived there till 1749 when he set up with his brother John in a house in Covent Garden. Perhaps Hunter bought them from the family after William George had abandoned medicine, perhaps he was given them in return for help in the family and care of Mrs Douglas's health. Nor were the papers and drawings the only Douglas material that passed into Hunter's possession. Douglas had built up "undoubtedly the best collection of practically useful anatomical preparations (acquired, prepared and preserved at a vast expense fatigue and care) that is or ever was in the possession of any single man". How far it formed the foundation of Hunter's own collection is not know but some Douglas material can be identified in Hunter's museum. Douglas books can also be identified in the Hunterian Library.

William Hunter must have obtained from Douglas's papers much of the inspiration for his own work. There is a large collection of papers on reproduction and on the anatomy of the gravid uterus. Douglas had long been contemplating a work on aneurisms and left notes on all those writers from Galen onwards who had written on the subject, one that was to interest Hunter for many years. Hunter's first paper to the Royal Society was on articular cartilages, on which he had been working for Douglas. Though little remains amongst his papers of Douglas's interest in hernias, it is known that he was contemplating a book on the subject. William Chesleden left a record of Douglas's interest in hernias and Hunter's involvement in this interest:

> I had this account of a hernia from the late Dr Douglas, a most industrious anatomist, very communicative, and much to be relied on, who was very clear they did not descend with the spermatic chord, but from the appearance thought that the whole was production of the peritoneum. The present case I have from Mr Hunter, a pupil of his ... .

This was an interest Hunter maintained and passed on to his brother John, which resulted in the dispute with Percival Pott. Perhaps no assessment of William Hunter's achievements should be attempted without a knowledge of James Douglas's papers.

Some of Douglas's papers were bound up, probably by William Hunter, and have been catalogued with Hunter's manuscripts by Young and Henderson (1908). The rest of the papers, together with Hunter papers and some extraneous material, were made at some time into thirty six packages. Kenneth Bryn Thomas, in 1964, published a brief life of James Douglas and catalogued the contents of the packages. He did excellent work in describing and accessing the significance of the papers but the limited time that he was able to spend in examining them and the fact that he was not permitted or did not feel justified in disturbing the contents of the different packages made it difficult for him to produce a comprehensive catalogue. Very great help however has been obtained from this initial catalogue. The Hunter and other materials have now been separated from the Douglas papers and it has been possible to reunite papers belonging together which had become separated and spread through several packages. This re-organisation and re-cataloguing of the papers has demonstrated more clearly the extraordinary breadth of Douglas's interests.

In attempting to give a full picture of Douglas's very wide interests, activities and achievements this new catalogue also contains references to Douglas papers held by other institutions and references to him from other sources. No attempt has been made to record the numerous occasions when Douglas showed specimens of clinical interest to the Royal Society. These are all recorded in the Journal Books of the Royal Society.

How much of the material acquired by Hunter may have been lost is not known. It would be surprising if nothing had disappeared. John Hunter had access to the papers and removed a collection of drawings of Douglas's dissection of the thornback (skate) which are now in the Library of the Royal College of Surgeons of England. He may have removed other material. Certainly the engraved plates for many of Douglas's printed figures which are known to have been sent to Glasgow have all disappeared. However, even if there have been losses, it is an impressive collection that remains.

Brief Biography of James Douglas

1675	Baptised at West Calder, Scotland.
1694	? MA Edinburgh University. ? Permission to go to Holland.
1698	Utrecht.
1699	MD Rheims.
1700	London, assistant to Paul Chamberlen.
1705	'Account of Valsalva's *De Aure Humana Tractatus* (1704)', *Phil. Trans.* **xxiv** 1978-1988.
1706	'An account of a very large tumour in the fore part of the neck', *Phil. Trans.* **xxv** 2214-2129. Started anatomy lectures. 'An account of a *hydrops ovari* with a new and exact figure of the *glandulae renales* and the uterus in a puerpera', *Phil. Trans.* **xxv** 2317-2324. Elected FRS, 4 December.
1707	*Myographia Comparatae Specimen or a Comparative Description of all the muscles in a Man and a Quadruped ... to which is added An Account of the Muscles peculiar to a woman,* London.
1710	'Of the dissection of a person who died of an ulcer in the right kidney', *Phil. Trans.* **xxvii** 32-35.
1712	Gale Lecturer in Osteology, Barber Surgeons' Company.
1714	*Bibliographical Anatomicae Specimen sive Catalogue Omnium pene Anatorum qui ab Hippocrate ad Harveum Rem Anatomieum ... scriptus illustrarat,* London.
1715	'An account of the left ventricle of the heart of an amazing magnitude', *Phil. Trans.* **xxix** 326-329.
1716	Arris Lecturer, Barber Surgeons' Company. 'Observations on the glands in the human spleen,

and a fracture in the upper part of the thigh bone', *Phil. Trans,* **xxix** 499-502.
'The natural history and description of the *Phaenicopterus* or Flamingo', *Phil. Trans.* **xxix** 523-541.

1720 Possibly it was in this year he was appointed Physician in Extraordinary to Caroline, Princess of Wales.

1721 Honorary Fellow, Royal College of Physicians.

1723 'A botanical description of the flower and seed vessel of the crocus *Autumnalis sativus*', *Phil. Trans,* **xxxii** 441-445.

1724 *Index Materia Medica or a Catalogue of Simple Medicines that are fit to be used in the Practice of Physic and Surgery,* London.

1725 *Lilium Sarniensis or a Description of the Guernsay-Lilly to which is added the Botanical Dissection of the Coffee Berry,* London.
At the end of this there was an advertisement:

> Whereas His Majesty has been graciously pleased by a Gratuity of five hundred pounds, to encourage and enable Dr James Douglas, Honorary Fellow of the *Royal College of Physicians* and Fellow of the *Royal Society* to communicate the Observation and Discoveries he has made in Anatomy both Human and Comparative ...

1726 *The History of the Lateral Operation or An Account of the Method of Extracting a Stone ...* , London.

French translation, 1726
Latin translation, 1733.

Involvement in the case of Mary Toft, the Rabbit-Woman of Godalming.

1727 *An Advertisement occasion'd by some passages in Sir R. Manningham's Diary, lately published,*

	London.
	Abor Yemensis Fructum Café Ferens; or a Description and History of the Coffee Tree, London.
	A Supplement to the Description of the Coffee Tree, London.
1728	'The culture and management of saffron in England', *Phil. Trans.* **xxxv** 566-574.
1729	*A Description of the Guernsey Lilly,* New Edition, London.
	'Of the different kinds of Ipecachuana', *Phil. Trans.* **xxxvi** 152-158.
1730	*A Description of the Peritoneum and of that Part of the Membrana Cellularis which lies on its Outside, with an Account of the True Situation of all the Abdominal Viscera, in respect of these two Membranes*, London.
1731	Reprint of *The History of the Lateral Operation with Appendix Containing Mr Cheselden's present method*, London.
1732	An abstract of a book entitled *A short Account of Mortifications and of the surprising Effects of the Bark in putting a stop to their Progress* [by John Douglas], *Phil. Trans.* **xxxvii** 429-433.
1733	Became governor of St Georges Hospital.
1734	Attending the Princess of Orange at Harwich.
1735	Attending the Princess of Orange in Holland. Granted a pension of £500 per annum by the King for his attendance on the Princess of Orange.
1737	Reprint of *A Description of the Guernsey Lilly* with a new introduction.
1739	Again in Holland attending the Princess of Orange.
1740	Exempted from paying the annual subscription to the Royal Society.

1741 William Hunter became his assistant and tutor to his son, William George.
Catalogus Editorum Quinti Horatii Flacci ab an 1476 ad an 1739, quae in bibliotheca Jacob Douglas ... adservantur, London.
The First Ode of Horace copied from a Ms in my Collection of the edition of his works. [Printed but not published].

1742 Croonian Lecturer, Royal Society.
2nd April, died.

William George Douglas

The few papers of James Douglas's son, William George, have been included in this hand list. Born in 1725, he became a medical student and attended Alexander Monro's anatomy lectures in Edinburgh in 1739 when he may have met William Hunter there. When Hunter joined the Douglas household in 1741 part of his employment was to act as tutor to William George. After his father's death, William Hunter helped him to put together his father's papers on the bladder, the subject of James Douglas's proposed second Croonian Lecture, which he then read to the Royal Society on 27 May 1742. In the autumn of 1743 he went with Hunter to Paris to attend anatomy lectures there. In 1748 he published *Nine Anatomical Figures representing the External Parts, Muscles and Bones of the Human Body*, based on drawings made by F. Boitand, for his father, from the works of Vesalius and Bidloo. Perhaps this represents an attempt to take in hand the publication of James Douglas's projected 'Osteology' for which all the figures had been completed and described, but William George carried the project no further. There is no evidence that he ever practised medicine. He died in debt in 1754. His nearest relatives refused to administer the estate; goods, chattels and credits were granted to Richard Holmes Esq., a creditor (PRO, PCS, Admon 1755). William Hunter is said to have lent him money on occasion.

Known pupils of James Douglas

George Douglas (1698-1736), brother, MD Rheims 1727, translator of Winslow's *Exposition Anatomique* (1732), dedicated to James Douglas. FRS 1732.

Robert Nesbitt (1697-1761), MD Leyden 1721, FRS 1725, author of *Human Osteology Explained in Two Lectures* (1736), dedicated to James Douglas, married the sister of Douglas's wife (Munk).

Joseph Hurlock, author of *Practical Treatise on Dentition, or the Breeding of Teeth in Children* (1742), dedicated to Douglas.

William Douglas (1710-1752), no relation, MD Rheims, physician to the Middlesex Hospital and physician to the Prince of Wales. Attacked William Smellie's midwifery practices.

James Parsons (1705-1770), MD Rheims 1736, FRS 1741, foreign secretary Royal Society, author of many papers and books (DBN).

William Hunter (1718-1783), MD Glasgow 1750, FRS 1767, author of a number of papers and of *The Anatomy of the Human Gravid Uterus* (1774). Hunter became the owner of the Douglas Papers and Figures.

Identified amanuenses

George Douglas, brother.

Israel James Douglas, son.

Walter Tullideph, doctor, botanist, went to the West Indies, corresponded with Sir Hans Sloane (*Proc. Bot. Soc. Br. Isl.* **vi**, 1967 312-13).

Samuel Boyse (1708-1775), minor poet, inventor of paper collars and cuffs, having sold his only shirt (DBN).

David Watson (1710-1756), published a prose version of Horace (DBN).

James Parsons.

William Hunter.

Where no amanuensis is given, the manuscript is in James Douglas's handwriting.

A number of manuscripts, mainly relating to grammar and language, are in childish copperplate handwriting and may be exercises by James Douglas's children, or transcriptions by them.

Artists and engravers who worked for James Douglas

Artist A

The earliest figures made for James Douglas were small, neat, rather diagrammatic figures in pencil and grey wash. None of these drawings are signed and there are no indications in James Douglas's papers as to who this artist was.

François Boitard (1670-1715)

A considerable number of figures dated between 1713 and 1715 are signed F. Boitard, and where the figures were engraved they were also engraved by him. Born in Holland, and a pupil of Raymond Lafage, he is described by Benezit as '*homme inquiet et debauché*', his best known work being a set of obscene engravings. He worked in Holland, France and England. The Louvre possesses eight pen and wash drawings by him, and examples of his work occur in other collections. As an anatomical artist he was a failure, his drawings in pen and wash are messy and dull.

Louis Pierre Boitard

Son of François Boitard and also a pupil of Raymond Lafage. Born in France, he came to England with his father and married an English woman. He became well known as an engraver of plates for books and of portraits. Though Vertue describes him as being employed by Dr Douglas on anatomical figures, there is only one engraving signed by him and one ink drawing, unsigned, which is similar in style to the engraving. From this example of his work it was clear, neat and diagrammatic.

Artist B - probably George Douglas.

After 1715 for some years Douglas employed an unknown artist whose work in pencil and wash was much more satisfactory in representing anatomical subjects, though it is competent rather than artistic. During this time Douglas was employing an amanuensis who was certainly his younger brother, George, FRS, died 1737. It could well be that George was also responsible for the figures, for the very occasional comments on the drawings appear to be in the handwriting of the amanuensis.

P. R. Fremont

During this same period there were also made for James Douglas a series of drawings in black and white chalk on grey papers. Some of these are signed P. R. Fremont. He was a Member of Parliament and an amateur artist and engraver. Portraits by him of John Alder and William Groves were published in James Caulfield, *Characters of remarkable persons from the Revolution in 1688 to the end of the reign of George II*, London (1879).

Artist C

For some time in the 1720s Douglas employed an artist who produced fine red crayon drawings, both of anatomical and botanical subjects. None of these drawings are signed. They are not only accurate but artistically attractive, and many of them were engraved for Douglas's projected 'Osteology' and for his botanical works. One set of drawings is contained in a folder made from a letter addressed to M. Claude Dubosc. Dubosc had been brought from France to England by Nicholas Dorigny to help him engrave the Raphael Cartoons. Dubosc left Dorigny but stayed in London where he eventually took a shop and sold prints. Some of the drawings have comments on them in French. All this suggests that Dubosc, if not responsible for the drawings, may have made some the osteological engravings.

Charles Dupuis

One engraving is signed by Charles Dupuis. He also was brought over from France by Nicholas Dorigny to help engrave the Raphael Cartoons. Subsequently he quarrelled with Dorigny and returned to France.

Bernard Baron (d. 1762)

Though there are neither drawings nor engraving signed by Baron in the collection, letters between Baron and Douglas show that he did some work for him. Baron was brought over from France by Claude Dubosc to help him engrave

The Story of Ulysses from designs by Rubens in Dr Richard Mead's possession.

Michael van der Gucht (1660-1725)

A native of Antwerp and pupil of Bouttats, he came to England and worked mainly engraving anatomical figures.

Gerard van der Gucht (b. 1697)

Son of Michael, he also specialised in engraving anatomical figures, including some of the plates for William Cheselden's *Osteographia* (1737). He was responsible for engraving the plates for James Douglas *Description of the Guernsay-Lilly* (1725) and (1729).

Artist D

Douglas had made a series of figures in pencil and wash showing stages in the development of the chick. While some of the figures look like the work of Artist B, those of the later stages of development are fine, lively figures, of a much higher quality than those of B.

James Parsons (1705-1770)

James Parsons, who eventually rose to some eminence in the medical profession and was elected a Fellow of the Royal Society, between 1736 and 1740 worked as anatomical assistant, amanuensis and artist for James Douglas. Working generally in red crayon, his figures are accurate but dull. Amongst other figures he made for Douglas were those of the rhinoceros that during 1739 was kept in Eagle Street, near Douglas's house in Red Lion Square.

Du Flos and Henriel

Two figures of the Scapula, one labelled 'Du Flos' and the other 'Henriel', almost certainly in the handwriting of Douglas's amanuensis A, taken to be that of his brother George, look like copies of figures of this bone made by two different artists. No Heriel is recorded as artist. There were at the end of the seventeenth and first half of the eighteenth century various artists with the name - Du Flos but none of them are recorded as having made anatomical figures.

R. Smith and N. Bundock

Nothing can be found about these two men. R. Smith engraved one of the early figures of bones and N. Bundock drew one of the skeleton drawings after Vesalius.

Piere Angillis (1685-1734)

James Douglas mentions that M. Angelis had made for him a drawing of a Guernsey lily bulb that had flowered a second time. This drawing has not survived. Angillis came to London about 1719 and remained there till 1727. He painted mainly landscapes with small figures into which he was fond of introducing fruit and fish.

Abbreviations

BT	Numbering of Douglas papers in K. Bryn-Thomas, *James Douglas of the Pouch and his Pupil William Hunter,* London (1962).
BL	British Library.
D	Douglas Papers.
DF	Douglas Figures.
DNB	*Dictionary of National Biography,* Leslie Stephens (ed.), London (1885).
DR	Douglas Records, correspondence relating to the Douglas Papers.
JB	Journal Book of the Royal Society.
L+P	Letters and Papers, Royal Society.
CP	Classified Papers, Royal Society.
RB	Record Book, Royal Society.
Munk	William Munck, *Roll of the Royal College of Physicians of London,* (1878) 3 volumes.
MsH	John Young and P. Henderson Aitken, *A Catalogue of the Manuscripts in the Library of the Hunterian Museum in the University of Glasgow,* Glasgow (1908).
MR	Hunterian Museum Records, Hunterian Library.
Teacher	John H. Teacher, *Catalogue of the Anatomical and Pathological Preparations of Dr William Hunter in the Hunterian Museum Glasgow University,* Glasgow (1900) 2 volumes.
WGD	William Douglas Papers.

References in square brackets [ ] indicate superseded listings: References in **bold face** and in round brackets ( ) are current call numbers

DOUGLAS PAPERS

Anatomy

Lectures

James Douglas started giving private lectures in anatomy in 1706.

D1 *An account of what Dr Douglas obliges himself to perform in a course of Human and Comparative Anatomy*, London (1706). pp 4. Transcription. Original was used by Douglas to make folders for case histories, see D194, D196.

D2 Part of set of notes for anatomy lectures. There is no positive evidence that these were for Douglas's advertised course, but their handwriting and format suggest that they date from Douglas's early years in London. p 20.

D3 In 1712 Douglas was elected to the Gale Osteology Lectureship of the Barber Surgeons' Company. Sidney Young in *Annals of the Barber Surgeons' Company* (1890) states that Dr Wadsworth was that year elected to the lectureship in preference to Dr Douglas. This is an error. The Minute Book of the Barber Surgeons' Company at the Guildhall, London, records Dr Douglas's election in preference to Dr Wadsworth. No printed syllabus for these lectures has survived.

D3.1 Draft of Gale lecture on bones of the tongue. p 1.

D3.2 Draft of Gale lecture on bones of the nasal region. p 1.

D3.3 Draft of Gale lecture on diseases of bone. p 1.

D3.4 Draft of final lecture. p 1.

D4 In 1716 Douglas was elected to the Arris Lectureship on Muscles at the Barber Surgeons' Company. For these a printed syllabus was published. Dr Douglas, in 1717, resigned from the lectureship owing to a disagreement with the Masters of anatomy.

Syllabus musculorum corpis Humani ... quo in Theatre Anatomico Collegii Chirurgorum Londinensium publice demonstrator, in sex Prelectiones distinctus, London (1716) with Ms notes by Douglas.

Bones

The significance of these papers is not known. They may have been meant for publication or they have been drafts for lectures.

D5 'Shoulder'
An account of what is meant by the word 'shoulder'.
Amanuensis, G. Douglas. pp 38.

D6 Part of a draft in two forms for D5.
Amanuensis, G. Douglas. pp 2 + 2.

D7 '*Os scapula latuis*, or the shoulder blade'
A description of the bone, its synonyms, uses, ligaments and muscular attachments.
Amanuensis, G. Douglas, with added notes by Douglas. pp 67. [BT 5.12]

D8 'Description of the shoulder, incomplete'
Section 5, 7, 9-21 (Draft for MsH Hunter 601).
Amanuensis, G. Douglas. pp 26.

D9 List of editions of Celsus with transcriptions from them of descriptions of scapula.
In coloured wrapper. pp 5.

D10 '*Os scapula latius*'
Bound Ms describing the shoulder
Amanuensis, G. Douglas, additional notes by Douglas. pp 62. [BT 6.9]

D11 Draft of pages 21-29 and top of page 30 of D10 which had been removed from the bound Ms D10.

D12 '*Clavicula*'
Description of the clavicle.
Amanuensis, G. Douglas. pp 22. [BT 5.12]

D13 '*Focile*'
"... bones of the forearm and leg ... have been unusually called focilia ..."
Amanuensis, G. Douglas. pp 12.

D14 '*Os humeri*'
An account of the bone under various headings.
Amanuensism, G Douglas. pp 12.

D15 αγκων
"This is a word very often used by Hypocrates and always in one of these two senses either for the whole joynt of the elbow... or for the olecranum alone ..."
An account of Greek words used to describe the elbow joint
Amanuensis, G. Douglas. pp 22.

D16 '*Radius*'
A description of the bone under various headings.
Amanuensis, G. Douglas. pp 14.

D17 '*Ulna*'
A description of the bone under various headings.
Amanuensis, G. Douglas. pp 23.

D18 Notes on Greek terms used by various authors to describe the bones and joints of the shoulder and arm.
Amanuensis, G. Douglas. pp 3.

D19 An account of the bones of the pelvic girdle.
Amanuensis, G. Douglas. pp 3.

D20 'The circumference of the patella'
Notes for his Ms. 'The Anatomy of the Patella' MsH 568 and 596.
Headings in childish hand, particulars filled in by Douglas.

D21 'Some observations made in dissecting a stiff joint of the knee'

Amanuensis, G. Douglas.
Part of draft for Ms with the same title, MsH 596.
pp 2. [BT 18.10]

D22 Rough notes on bones. pp 3.

D23 Notes on writers on bones of the nasal region.
Possibly for 'Of the nasal bones' MsH 545. pp 31.
[BT 10.2]

D24 An index relating to aspects of osteology - of unknown significance.
Amanuensis, G. Douglas. pp 26.

D25 'Bones'
References to authors where they mention certain bones.
Amanuensis, G. Douglas. p 1.

D26 '*Coiterus*'
Notes in Latin on Coiter on bones. p 1.

D27 Notes on 'Observations Osteologiques' by M. Winslow, *Memoires de l'Academie Royale*, (1772) 327.
Amanuensis, G Douglas. p.1.

George Douglas published *An Anatomical Exposition of the Structure of the Human Body*. London (1732). Translated from the French original by Jaques Benigne Winslow. A copy of the original was given by Winslow to James Douglas.

D28 Recto - Index to references to diseases of bones.
Verso - References to a variety of diseases.
Amanuensis, G. Douglas. p 1.

D29 Notes on bones from an unidentified author.
Amanuensis not known. pp 5.

D30 Notes on the femur from various authors.
Amanuensis not known. pp 9.

D31 Account of a book, viz. *De Aure Humana Tractatus* ... by Antonio Maria Valsalva M.D. (1704). pp 14.
Draft for a paper reviewing this book, read to the

Royal Society by Douglas and published in *Phil. Trans.* **xxiv** (1705) 1978-85.
A copy of this book was sent to Sir Hans Sloane by G. Stephey, 5 May 1705, from Vienna (B.L. Sloane Ms 40414 f31). Perhaps Sloane gave it to Douglas to review. It was Sir Hans Sloane, who in 1706, recommended Douglas for a Fellowship of the Royal Society.

Bound Mss on bones

Probably intended for the great Osteology that he was planning

'Introduction to Osteology'
Amanuensis, G. Douglas. MsH 544.
This represents the final form derived from three earlier drafts, MsH 592, MsH 548 and MsH 567, of an historical introduction to Douglas's proposed great Osteology.

'General Osteology'
Amanuensis, G. Douglas. MsH 592.

'Osteology of the Antients'
Amanuensis, G. Douglas. MsH 548.

'Osteology of the Antients'
Amanuensis, G. Douglas. MsH 567.

'History of Osteological figures'
Amanuensis, G. Douglas. MsH 566.

'A Lexicon or Explanation of the Greek terms of Osteology'
Amanuensis, G. Douglas. MsH 558.

'Diseases of Bones'
Amanuensis, G. Douglas. MsH 547.

'This is the Authors in order of time and the place in them marked where they mention the diseases of bones.'
Amanuensis, G. Douglas. MsH 563.

'The Anatomy of the Patella or the Description of the moveable bone of the knee considered in a

natural state with figures after life by J. D.'
Amanuensis, G. Douglas, notes by J. Douglas.
MsH 568.
Containing also
'Some observations made in Dissecting a stiff joint of the knee'.
Amanuensis, James Parsons.
And
A letter from John Shipton to James Douglas, 5 Mar. 1724/5 on the patella and on the possibility of Douglas publishing a work on hernias.

'On the Patella'.
Amanuensis, James Parsons. MsH 596.
A contracted form of MsH 568, with descriptions of the figures in DF33.
Containing also
'Some observations made in dissecting a stiff joint of the knee'.
Amanuensis, G. Douglas.
And
'Some remarks upon a transverse fracture of the Patella'
Read before the Royal Society, 14 Nov. 1724.
Amanuensis, James Parsons.
The JB records this paper as given on 1 Jan. 1724/25. There is added in the JB and then crossed out:

"if this memoire be thought worthy of a place in the printed Transactions I will willingly consent to have it inserted but I must beg to be excused from parting with the figures that relate to it. These I reserve for the history of the Patella which I intend in a very short time to publish."

It was not published in *Phil. Trans*. This may have been a transcription of the original paper because Parsons did not start working for Douglas till 1736.

The remaining bound Mss may relate to Douglas's anatomy lectures, or to the project, mentioned in his introduction to *Myographia Comparata* (1707), to publish small anatomical handbooks on all six parts of anatomy, i.e. bones, muscles, nerves, glands, alimentary system and reproductive system, of which only that on muscles was published.

'Description of Bones'
Amanuensis, G. Douglas. MsH 556.

'Description of Bones'
Incomplete. Amanuensis, G. Douglas. MsH 589.

'Description of the human skeleton from the bones of the pelvis inclusive downwards'
Amanuensis, G. Douglas. MsH 590.

'Of the Nasal Bones'
Amanuensis, G. Douglas. MsH 545.
From contained references it must be post 1724.

'Description of the bones with their ligaments and attachments of muscles of the upper extremity'
Amanuensis, G. Douglas. MsH 601.

Muscles

In 1707 Douglas published *Myographa Comparata specimen or a Comparative description of all the muscles in a man and a quadruped ... to which is added an account of the muscles peculiar to a woman*. None of the surviving manuscript material is a draft of this work.

D32 'In order to describe a muscle ...'
Ten points to be considered.
Amanuensis, G. Douglas. pp 4.

D33 Notes on the Muscles, with an index.
Section 6 missing.
Amanuensis, G. Douglas. pp 42.

D34 'A description of the Muscles'
Amanuensis, G. Douglas. pp 115.

D35 Different descriptions of some of the muscles in D34.
Amanuensis, G. Douglas. pp 14.

D36 'Scapula'.
Notes of a dissection(?) of muscles associated with the scapula, arm and hand.
Partly in Douglas's hand, partly in that of possibly his cousin Kennaway.

D37 Notes of a dissection(?) of the muscles of the shoulder. pp 3.

D38 '*Musculi cutanei*'
Notes of dissection(?) of muscles of the skin, adomen, ribs, intestines, etc. 13 Nov. pp 4.

D39 Notes of a dissection(?) of muscles of neck and back. pp 2 [BT 10.2E]

D40 Recto - Notes on muscles of the hand. James Douglas.
Verso - Notes on muscles of the leg. Kennaway. p 1.

D41 Under headings of muscles by James Douglas, notes by James Douglas and unidentified hand. pp 4. [BT 19.6]

D41.4 reused from notes on medicinal plants.

D42 In a wrapper labelled by James Douglas '*Coraco-humeralis alter*'.
Under headings written by James Douglas, notes on muscles of the arm and hand by William Hunter. pp 118 [BT 6.1]

Letters to James Douglas from:-

D42.11 Part of a letter from C. Keil, Stratford on Avon, Warwickshire, ND.
D42.27 Jno. Blackstone, Fleet Street, 30 Dec. 1740.
D42.30 Alex Monro, 15 Oct. 1740.
D42.43 Part of a letter from Watford, 5 Oct. 1740.
D42.45 M. F. Collingwood, 25 July 1741.
D42.49 Alex Gordon, ND.
D42.51 M. Whitehall, ND.
D42.85 Lew Theobald, 8 May 1741.

D42.102	Eliz Jones, Saturday morning.
D42.106	Nat Gould, ND.
D42.110	W. Russell, Grocers Alley, 29 Aug. 1733.
D42.115	Edward Murdoch, Chertsey, 9 July 1741.
D42.8b	To Mr John Chandler, from Tho. Whyte, 5 June 1741.

D43 Miscellaneous notes on muscles.
Amanuensis, G. Douglas. pp 9.

D44 Notes on authors under headings of the various muscles.
Amanuensis, G. Douglas. pp 63.

D45 Scrap of paper with list of muscles under author headings.

D46 '*Sacculi mucosi*'
Draft of account that occurs in 'The Anatomy of the Patella'. MsH 568.
Amanuensis, G. Douglas. pp 4. MsH 568.
Douglas was the first to describe these mucus sacs. See *William Hunter's Lectures on Anatomy*, Elsevoir, Amsterdam (1972) p 27.

D47 '*Sacculi mucosi*'
Notes on the mucus sac between the two ligaments connecting the *processes coracoides* to the clavicle.
Amanuensis, G. Douglas. p 1.

D48 *'Historia Anatomica'*
History of the descriptions of the muscles of the scapula, pectoral region, etc.
Amanuensis, G. Douglas. pp 53. [BT 5.3, 5.4]

D49 Notes on intercostal muscles partly by James Douglas, partly in an unidentified hand.
'Loose Papers B', probably 19th century labelling, in folder made from *Daily Post*, 19 Oct. 1738.
pp 19. [BT 5.1]

D50 'Additional observations concerning the muscles of the abdomen'
Account of a dissection of a female.
Amanuensis, G. Douglas. pp 4.

D51 Part of a description of the *vastus externus*.
Amanuensis, G. Douglas. p 1.

D52 '*Pronator Radii Teres*'
An account of some of the muscles of the shoulder, elbow and hand, one section dated 5 July 1729.
Amanuensis, G. Douglas. pp 63.

D53 'A new description of the interosseous muscles of the hand by J. D.'
Two versions of this paper, together with notes on the subject.
The description reads as if it was intended to be given to the Royal Society but the JBs record no such paper, though this is not conclusive evidence that the paper was not given.
Text amanuensis, G. Douglas, one section dated 12 Dec. 1728; notes, G. Douglas and James Douglas.
pp 39 of text, 6 of notes. [BT 5.13]

D54 Part of description of the muscles of the pelvic girdle.
Amanuensis, G. Douglas. pp 2.

D55 '*Ligamentum Falloppii*'
An account of the ligament.
Amanuensis, G Douglas. pp 8.

Anatomy of the soft parts of the body

In 1730 Douglas published his most important work on anatomy, *A description of the peritoneum and that part of the membrana cellularis which lies on its outside. With an account of the true situation of all the abdominal viscera, in respect of these two membranes,* London.

D56 In a wrapper labelled by William Hunter
'No 68 [Peri]toneum viz. (A description of the) Miscellaneous observations in Anatomy:
This First Contains a Description of the

Peritoneum'.
An early draft of the published work together with the draft of a dedicatory letter to Dr Mead. Douglas's name is associated with a fold in the peritoneum between the rectum and the bladder 'The Pouch of Douglas' - in this draft Douglas acknowledges the priority of Winslow in the description of this fold (D56.60 verso) but this is left out in the printed version. pp 87 with correction and addition slips.

D56.1 Letter to James Douglas from N. Lawton, 23 July 1730.

D57 Schemes, notes and drafts for work on the peritoneum.
Amanuensis, G. Douglas. pp 33.

D57.3 Letter to James Douglas from Robert Lawley, Marlbro Street, 23 Jan. 1729/30.

'Of the Peritoneum', MsH 565.
The first section reads like a paper to the Royal Society but the JB records no such paper.

D58 '*Vesicula*'
A description of the bladder and its peritoneal covering.
Almost certainly from its style this belongs to MsH 565, which lacks a section on the peritoneal covering of the bladder.
Amanuensis, G. Douglas. pp 10.

'Miscellaneous observations in Anatomy, Part 1, Of the Peritoneum', MsH 543.
This is the manuscript of the published work, though the dedication to Dr Richard Mead is not quite the same. Related figures in DF130.

D60 'The history, description and use of a new salivary duct that opens about the middle of the root of the tongue and there discharges a liquor separated by the many glands seated in the neighbourhood of the mouth, with a view of some of the principal parts of that cavity as they appear in one affected

with venereal disease compared with the same parts in their natural state and condition by J.D.', 14 Dec. 1721.
A review of Abraham Vater, *Novum ductum salivatem* ... Wittenborgae (1720), used in proposing Vater as a F R.S. (JB, 14 Dec. 1721). pp 4. [BT 5.10]

D61 'The *Ductus Thoracicus Lymphae Chyloque communis*, described and demonstrated in human subject by J.D.', 12 Mar. 1723/24.
A bound Ms, together with part of a draft of the same and part of a fine copy of a paper to the Royal Society on 12 Mar. 1724/25 (JB).
Bound Ms, partly in James Douglas's hand, partly in Walter Tulideph's, pp 14; draft, James Douglas's hand, p 1; fine copy, amanuensis, Walter Tulideph, pp 3. [BT 5.9]

D62 Notes on authors on the thoracic duct.
James Douglas and Walter Tulideph, pp. 12.

The Croonian Lectures

"Dr Douglas being desired by Sir Hans Sloane Bart to read the Croonian Lectures on Muscular Motion for the year 1741 did now communicate his first exercise thereon." (JB, 18 Mar. 1741/42).

James Douglas's Croonian Lecture on the '*Membrana palati mobilis*, the *uvula* and the *tuba Eustachiana*'. (L+P 1.69).
Introduction in Douglas's hand, the rest of the paper in William Hunter's writing.
No draft for this lecture survives in the Douglas papers, but there are relevant notes.

D63 Notes on the Eustachian tube.
Mainly on scraps of paper and old letters.
In James Douglas's hand, some notes by William Hunter. pp 20.

Letters to James Douglas from:

D63.2 W Oliver, Bath, 9 Nov. 1741.
D63.3 John Blackstone, 26 Dec. 1741.
D63.4 Sam London, ND (2 letters).
D63.9 R. Mead, 16 Dec.
D63.10 D. Mallet, ND.
D63.12 Ann Powell, ND.
D63.15 John Campbell, ND (part of letter).
D63.19 Letter asking for help in getting situation as wet nurse, ND.
D63.19 Note to Sir William Young, possibly from Lord Torrington, relating to Eliz Jones.

Also advertisement for Joseph Hurlock, *A Practical Treatise upon Dentition or the Breeding of Teeth in Children,* London (1742). Hurlock had been a pupil of James Douglas. [BT 6.3]

D64 '*Uvula*'
Notes on authors who had described the uvula and an index of writers on the ethmoid bone. Amanuensis, G. Douglas, therefore must predate the Croonian lectures by some years. pp 22. Related figures in DF 121.
According to a note by William Hunter in D66, Douglas's second Croonian Lecture was to have been on the bladder, but he died before it was delivered. Hunter helped William George Douglas, James Douglas's son, to organise a paper from his father's notes. Some of Douglas's interest in the bladder relates to his interest in lithotomy.

D65 Notes on the bladder, pp 9.

Letters to James Douglas from:

D65.4 J. Campbell, first half of letter in D63.15.
D65.5 J. Van Harthals, 13 Jan.
D65.8 W. Maclean, Aldersgate St., 4 Mar. 1741.

D66 William Hunter's notes on the bladder and on authors who had written on the bladder, under headings, and with additions by James Douglas, pp 52.

Letters to James Douglas from:
D66.7 G. W Tessier, 20 Jan. 1741/2.
D66.8 Sophia King, Ormond Street, Wednesday.

D67 Notes on the bladder by William George Douglas and draft of his paper to the Royal Society. pp 18. [BT 12.2]

William George Douglas read 'Of the Bladder' to the Royal Society on 27 May 1742. The paper had been written out by William Hunter (L+P 1.100).

'Of the membrana urinaria in a human placenta by J. D.' (CP, xii, {ii} 22).
Here attributed to John Douglas

'Of the Bladder'
Amanuensis, William Hunter.

According to William Hunter (D66) James Douglas's third Croonian Lecture was to have been on the larynx. From Douglas's papers it is suggested that this third lecture was to cover a much wider field.

At some earlier date an abstract of Antoine Ferrein's Memoire on the Glottis from the *Memoires de l'Académie Royale des Sciences*, Paris, had been read to the Royal Society and then handed over to James Douglas to review (JB, 10 Dec. 1741).

D68 Notes and drafts dated 14 Jan. 1741/42, with comments on Ferrein's Memoire, for a paper to the Royal Society in Douglas's and William Hunter's hands. pp 13 [BT 6.7]
The JB does not record this paper as having been read.

Letters of James Douglas from:
D68.3 Jas Keil, ND.

D68.6 W. Barwick, Warwick, 1741.
D68.8 G. W. Tessier, 19 Jan. 1741/42.
D68.10 D. Mallet, ND.
D68.12 A. Lee, The Green, Doretrash Street, Gray's Inn Lane, 17 Dec.
D68.13 John Blackstone, 19 Dec. 1741.

D69 Draft and notes in Douglas's and Hunter's hands for Douglas's Croonian Lecture: 'The Comparative Anatomy of the *Aspera Arteria* or Wind pipe in men and in Brutes', which was never given. Douglas mentions the recent election of Martin Folkes as president of the Royal Society. Related figures DF121. pp 26 [BT 6.6]

Letters to James Douglas from:
D69.7 Fragment.
D69.10 J Woollaston, ND.
D69.11 B. Greenwood, 27 Dec. 1741.
D69.12 James Green, ND.
D69.13 J. Scott, 16 Dec.

Miscellaneous notes on anatomy

D70 *'Puncta Lachrymalia'*
Notes on the authors who described this structure.
Amanuensis, G. Douglas. pp 2.

D70a Notes on the structure of the eye. p 1.
Verso - letter from George Garner, ND.

'A short description and demonstration of the parts of the eye affected by the *fistula lachrymalis'*, 24 Dec. 1713 (CP xii {1} 73).

D71 'The History of the *membrana carnosa*'
Headings by James Douglas.
Text amanuensis, G. Douglas. pp 12. [BT 5.8]

D72 '*Neuroligia*'
Possibly notes of a dissection of cranial nerves or notes for a lecture, and notes on the vessels branching off from the aorta. pp 4.

D73 Notes on Meri on the circulation of the blood through the heart of the foetus. p 1. [BT 22.14]

D74 Notes from *Memoirs de l'Académie Royale des Sciences, pour année 1699*, 23 Dec. On the circulation of blood in the foetus, and the heart of the frog. In French.
And notes on Rivius [Walther Hermann Ryff] in Latin.

D75 Notes on 'the parenchymous parts of the body'. p 1. Verso - a letter from the wife of James Douglas's brother, Walter. ND.

D76 Notes on the blood system.
30 May 1722, possibly dissecting notes. pp 7.

D77 Notes on the blood system, including extracts from authors, etc.
Amanuensis, James Parson. pp 36.

Bibliography of anatomy

In 1715 James Douglas published *Bibliographiae anatomicae specimen sive catalogus omnium pene Anatorum qui ab Hippocrate ad Harvaeum rem anatomicam ... Scriptis illustrarunt ...* Leiden (1715). This gives brief biographical details of the various anatomical authors and lists of their published works. In the body of the work the authors are arranged chronologically. There are two indexes, one arranged alphabetically according to Christian names of the author, the other according to last name.

D78 List of anatomical authors, with brief biographical details and publications.
Arranged alphabetically by first name. p 1.

D79 Extensive list of anatomical authors, arranged alphabetically by first name. Abielle to John; and Thomas to Zacharius. pp 51. [BT 9.3]

'*Biographia Anatomica*' MsH 611.
Bound manuscript, entitled by William Hunter, but it is not the manuscript for Douglas's *Biographiae*

Anatomicae. It has the authors arranged alphabetically by first name.

D80 Anatomical authors listed alphabetically by first name.
Amanuensis not identified. pp 6. [BT 9.4]

D81 Anatomical authors listed chronologically, Mundinus to Andreas Laurentius.
Amanuensis not identified. pp 2.

D82 Anatomical authors listed chronologically under the organs they described. pp 12. [BT 5.11]

D83 Three lists of anatomical authors arranged chronologically:
i. Hippocrates to William Harvey, 1628.
ii. Rhases, 1070, to Schelhammerus, 1652.
iii. Bonetus, 1675, to W. Cheselden, 1711.
Amanuensis of i. and ii. as in D 462, additions by James Douglas. pp 9.

D84 '*Catalogus authorae qui ex professo de auditus organo pertractant*'. p 1.

D85 '*Elenchus thematum anatomicorum quis a scriptoribus in hoc opere de scriptis, tractantitis ordine alphabetice dispositu*'.
Partly by Douglas, partly amanuensis as in D83. pp 31.

D86 Anatomical authors under country of origin.
Amanuensis as in D83, additions by James Douglas. pp 7.

D87 Notes on anatomists in Latin.
Amanuensis as in D83. additions by James Douglas. pp 10.

D88 Anatomical authors listed:
i. Alphabetically by first name.
ii. Alphabetically by last name.
iii. Chronologically by year of publication.
iv. By country of origin.
v. By subject.

Douglas's hand, with occasional notes by amanuensis as in D83. pp 44.

D89 '*Vocabularium anatomi cum ex Cl:Vesalio ordine abecidario dispositum*'
Amanuensis as in D83. pp 4.

D90 *Index rerum Anatomicaeii*
Index to an unidentified anatomical work. p 1.

D91 Three scraps of paper with names of anatomical or medical authors.

Surgery

Lithotomy

James Douglas was interested in the anatomical foundations of various branches of surgery. He collaborated with his brother John, in working out the necessary anatomical details for John's development of the 'high' operation for the removal of stones from the bladder.

> On 23 January 1717/18 he gave to the Royal Society a paper on 'The History and manner of performing that difficult and dangerous operation called Lithotomy' (JB). The manuscript of this paper has not survived.

At the end of John Douglas's *Lithotomia Douglassiana or a new method of cutting for the stone,* London (1723), John remarks:

> "I should have been more particular in the Description of these parts, did not my Brother Dr Douglas design speedily to oblige the world with a full and correct Description, not only of the Parts concerned in this, but also of these in all the other ways of cutting."

The book also carried the advertise that:

> "There will be published in a short time a Treatise intitled *Hernias* ... to which will be added The Anatomy of the parts cut, dilated, and tore in all the different methods of extracting a *Stone*

out of the human *Bladder*; whether above or below the *Os Pubis;* read at a meeting of the *Royal Society,* 13 January, An. 1717/18. By Dr James Douglas, Honorary Fellow of the *Royal college of Physicians, London* and Fellow of the *Royal Society.*"

The work was never published. James, however, continued to expand the project. In 1726 he published:

> *The History of the lateral operation: or an account of the method of extracting a stone by making a wound near the great protuberance of the os ischium... with a post-script concerning the introduction and improvement of this method in London,* London.

The following papers may relate to this work:

D92 'The Preface'
Possibly a draft of a preface not used in the published work. p 1.

'The various methods of lithotomy classed from the parts cut'. MsH 557.
This, after a general account of the different methods of extracting stones from the bladder, deals in more detail with the lateral operation

'An Historical Account of the Different methods of cutting for the Stone'. MsH 551.
This is very similar to MsH 557 but is extended to cover William Cheselden's development of the lateral operation.

In his introduction to his *History of the lateral operation* (1726) Douglas remarks:

> "I must further acquaint the Reader, that I intend that the History of this lateral operation shall be followed in a very short time, by that of the other three general Methods of cutting for the *Stone*, in three separate Treatises. To these I shall add a fifth containing the Anatomy and Figures of the Parts concerned in them all: the

figures of all the instruments that have been used: and lastly my own Observations concerning the Advantages and Inconveniences with which each of them are attended; and in what cases I judge any of them, taken all together, to be preferable to the rest."

"Dr Douglas communicated a paper containing an account of the whole process of the operation of cutting for the stone according to the way and method at present used by Mr Cheselden." (JB, 12 Nov. 1730).

Subsequently this was published as:

An appendix to the History of the lateral operation for the stone, containing Mr Cheselden's present method of performing it, London (1731).

But there was no further publication on lithotomy covering the other methods of extracting stones from the bladder.

D93 Drafts differing more or less from the published version of the *Appendix.*
Amanuensis, G. Douglas, with parts by James Douglas and other unidentified hands. pp 131.

D93.121 Letter to James Douglas from Samuel Jaques, 9 May 1731.

D94 'An appendix to the history of the lateral operation for the stone'
Drafts similar, except for occasional phrases, to the published version; together with proofs of the published plate, missing from the Hunterian Library copy of this work. [BT 12.1]

Though Douglas published nothing further on the subject, he maintained an interest in it, particularly in Celsus's method of operating for the stone.

'A methodized Account of Celsus's operation for the Stone'. MsH 522.
Section I, Introduction, Article I.
Description of the bladder in men.
Amanuensis, G. Douglas. pp 62 + 3 plates.

D95 Description of the bladder.
A more extended account of Celsus's operation than is given in MsH 522.
Amanuensis, G. Douglas. pp 72

'Reflections on Celsus's Account of Lithotomy' MsH 550.
Amanuensis, G. Douglas.

D96 Draft of parts of MsH 550.
Amanuensis, G. Douglas. pp 2.

'An Enquiry into the meaning of a very difficult passage in Celsus in his account of the operation for the stone' MsH 549.
Amanuensis, G. Douglas.

D97 Notes and rough draft for MsH 549.
Amanuensis, G. Douglas. pp 38.

Because the amanuensis was G. Douglas, these Mss must date from between 1720 and early 1730. The following four Mss, in the handwriting of David Watson, must date from the end of the 1730's.

'An Account of Celsus's operation for the stone' MsH 523.
Amanuensis, David Watson.

D98 Comments on Celsus's operation for the stone.
Amanuensis, David Watson. pp 16.

D99 Notes on later classical and Arabian writers on lithotomy.
Amanuenses, G. Douglas and David Watson. pp 18.

'History of Lithotomy' MsH 524.
A continuation of MsH 523, carrying on the history of lithotomy beyond the classical and Arabian writers. Mainly concerned with the *Apparatus major* operation.
Amanuensis, David Watson.

D100 Notes on Sanctus Marianus Barolitanus.
Amanuensis, G. Douglas. pp 3.

D101 Notes on the various editions of the works of Celsus.
Amanuenses, G. Douglas and David Watson, with additions by Douglas. pp 11.

Parts of letter to James Douglas:
D101.2 The vine, 23 Nov. 1729.
D101.3 23 Nov. 1738. This scrap of letter, was used by David Watson; suggesting the time Watson was working for Douglas.

D102 In a wrapper labelled by James Douglas 'The Old papers. Celsus'
Notes on Celsus and lithotomy.
Also labelled Part II, almost certainly 19C marking.
Amanuenses, G. Douglas and David Watson, additions by James Douglas. Included also what appear to be translations, in unidentified handwriting, of unidentified writings. pp 40.

Letters to James Douglas from:
D102.4 Robert North, ND.
D102.9 S Boyse. 10 Nov. 1738.
D102.10 Jno World, 25 May 173?
D102.11 Cuthbert Cunstable, ND.
D102.12 Mary Tunstall.

D103 Notes on writers on lithotomy.
Amanuenses, G. Douglas and two unidentified hands, additions by James Douglas. pp 32.

Letters to James Douglas from:
D103.1 W.T. 6 Jan.
D103.2 - 26 July 1727.
D103.17 Alex Stuart, ND.
D103.6 Draft of note by James Douglas.
D103.12 Advertisement for the sale of Bath and Bristol Hot Spring Waters.

D104 In a wrapper labelled on the outside 'No 7 Celsus' operation', and on the inside 'Celsus' operation

corrected'.
'Mistakes about Celsus operation for the stone'.
Under headings by James Douglas, comments written by David Watson. pp 8.

'On the high operation for the stone' MsH 591.
Amanuensis, G. Douglas.

D105 In a wrapper labelled by James Douglas '*Catalogus Autorum, De alto Apparate*'.
List of authors with titles of their works, arranged chronologically. Fuller than that which occurs at end of MsH 591.
Amanuensis, G. Douglas. pp 13.

D106 'Advertisement'
Draft of advertisement for a work on the parts concerned in the different methods of lithotomy this part refers to Celsus's operation.
Amanuensis, G. Douglas. pp 33.

D107 'A description of the parts concerned in the different methods of cutting in the stone'
Amanuensis, G. Douglas. pp 88.

D108 Two drafts of an article about a distended bladder.
Amanuensis, G. Douglas. pp 4.

D109 'A general view of the instruments used in the different methods of cutting, for the stone in as far as they have been hitherto represented by figures'.
Amanuensis, G. Douglas. pp 8.
Together with illustrations of the instruments of:-

i. Marianus.
ii. De Franco.
iii. Paré.
iv. Rossetus.
v. Hildanus.
vi. Scultelus, missing. (The only published figures are in *Armamentarium Chirurgicum* xliii, Ulmae 1655, plate xxxx.)
vii. Tolet.

viii. Groenveldt (they were not illustrated, presumably since they are the same as Tolet's).

ix. Solinghen (again similar to Tolets, and not illustrated).

x. Mery, missing (the conductor is illustrated in *Observations sur la manière de tailler dans les deux sexes pour l'extraction de la Pierre*, Paris (1700) p 18).

xi. Dionis missing (illustrated in *Cours d'opérations de Chirurgie* ... , 2nd edn, Paris, 1714).

xii. John Douglas, missing (illustrated in *Phil. Trans.* **xxxi**, 1722/23, 83).

xiii. William Cheselden.

D110 In a wrapper labelled by William Hunter. 'Instruments of Lithotomy' 26 miscellaneous prints and drawings of surgical instruments. Sources mainly unidentified. [BT Packet Q]

'Part of a letter giving an account of some things printed and to be printed' MsH 540.
Draft of a letter to J G. Stergerthal, physician to George I, who returned to Germany after the King's death in 1725. In this Douglas says "by the same conveyance which carries you this letter you will receive four printed pieces. A description of the Peritoneum 1730, An historical account of the different methods of lithotomy, An enquiry into the meaning of a difficult passage in Celsus's Description of the operation for the stone and an account of Mr Cheselden's new method of cutting".

Possibly 'An historical account' may refer to *The History of the lateral operation*, (1726) and 'an account of Mr Cheselden's new method' to *Appendix containing Mr Cheselden's present method* (1731) but while manuscript material exists for 'An enquiry into the meaning of a very difficult passage in Celsus' (D96) there is no evidence that this was ever published.

D111 Draft of part of MsH 540.
Amanuensis, G. Douglas. pp 2.

D112 Part of a transcription or draft of *A short essay on the operation of Lithotomy as it is performed by the new method above the Os pubis, to which is added a letter relating to the same subject from Mr Macgill of Edinburgh to Dr Douglas,* London (1727).
Handwriting not identified. pp 3. [BT 25.9]

Original drawings for plate 1 of this publication, a copy of the plate, and a description of the plate by James Douglas.

Aneurisms

Douglas had been interested in aneurism since at least the 1720s. In 1728 he read a paper to the Royal Society on 'A remarkable case of an aneurism from the Memoirs of the Royal Academy of Sciences (M. Littre)' (CP xii {ii} 40).

D113 Draft of part of the paper to the Royal Society.
Amanuensis, G. Douglas. pp 6.

D114 Aneurism.
Notes on authors on aneurisms.
Amanuensis, G. Douglas. pp 4.

Some time after 1736 Douglas started working on an extensive treatise on aneurisms. In this he was assisted by James Parsons.

D115 'A treatise of Aneurisms'.
The Contents.
Plan of the proposed work in James Parson's hand.
pp 2. [BT 24.1]
The headings of sections are given with relevant Mss listed below.

Part 1. 'A description of the coats of an Artery from Authors'
Part of a note by Douglas on Galen on the structure of arteries.

Part 2. 'My own dissection of an artery with a particular description of the Arch of curvature of the aorta and of the Arteries in the flexure of the cubit'
No relevant manuscripts, relevant figures by James Parson, DF115 and 119.

Part 3. 'The various opinions of authors reduced to a certain number of classes, in which everything new in each Author is particularly observed and set down in the order of time, in which it was published'

Many notes but no organised manuscript: the following papers are relevant.

D116 *Arteria ex Galeno* (fragment) and Wiseman on aneurisms. p 1.

D117 Extensive notes, mainly by James Douglas, on how the different types of aneurisms are classified, with notes on the authors who had described them. pp 30.

Letters to James Douglas from:
D117.1 B. Baron, ND.
D117.13 Fragment, 17 Aug. 1736 .
D117.18 Mary Ogilvy, 1 Apr. 1737.
D117.22 Jane Garbrand, 4 Apr. 1737.
D117.28 Fragment.

D118 'Writers on the first type of Aneurism, from a rupture of all the coats of an artery'. Amanuensis, James Parson. pp 26.

D119 Lists classes of aneurisms with brief descriptions of them by various authors.
Amanuensis, James Parsons. pp 18 [BT 24.1]

D120 Similar in contents to D119 but much fuller.
Amanuensis, James Parsons, with corrections and additions by James Douglas. pp 68.

Letters to James Douglas from:
D120.14 Fragment, Sunday 18 July .

D120.15 Joseph Lewin, Crown Court, Cheapside, ND.

D121 Aneurisms classified as in previous drafts, with transcriptions from various authors.
Headings by James Douglas, transcriptions by James Parsons. pp 41.

Part 4. A classical and chronological Table showing in one view the Sentiments of every author, together with the year in which his works were published.

D122 A fair copy of Parts 3 and 4 of the scheme.
Amanuensis, James Parsons. pp 41.

D123 A précis of D122.
Amanuensis, James Parsons. pp 4.

D124 Drafts by James Douglas for section 4, some of which has been incorporated into D122. pp 4.

Letters to James Douglas from:
D124.2 J. Blakey, Greenwich, 22 Mar. 1736.
D124.3 M. Gower, ND.

Part 5. 'A short methodical account of Aneurisms considered under the following heads'
viz. *Nomen, Synonima, Etymologia, Definitio, Devisio, Causa, Diagnosis, Prognosis, Cura.*

D125 Material collected for this section of the treatise.
In James Parson's hand with addition by James Douglas. pp 39. [BT 24.1]

Part 6. 'The Anatomical Dissection of two internal Aneurisms, one from a single Dilation of the Aorta, the other with a large Bagg, of the same substance with the vessel itself; being both seated in the great arch or curvature of the Aorta magna'
No relevant manuscript material but figures by James Parsons in DF118 may be relevant.

Part 7. 'A collection of several observations and dissections of the same kinds from Authors'

D126 Accounts of cases of aneurisms from various authors.
Amanuensis, James Parsons.

Part 8. 'Three figures representing the course of the veins, Arteries and nerves in the Bend of the Elbow, together with a fair delineation of the aponeurosis of the tendon of the Biceps muscle'.
Relevant drawings, DF119.

D127 In a folder labelled by James Douglas '*Venae Brachii*'.
Notes on the veins of the arm by James Douglas and James Parsons. pp 10. [BT 5.5]

Letters to James Douglas from:
D127.4 J. Anderson, Michaelsten, 1 Aug.
D127.8 M. Bressan, ND.

D128 Notes on the arteries and nerves of the arm on back of a letter from Jane Prince, 17 Sept. 1737.

Part 9. 'The course of the Aorta within the Thorax, in several views, fairly exhibited'
Relevant figures by James Parsons, DF 114.

Part 10. 'A Draught of the dilated Aorta and of the aneurismal Bagg expressed by several figures'
Relevant figures, DF118.

Part 11. 'A chronological Table of the editions of all the Authors mentioned in this Treatise, with full references to the chapter and page where the thing treated of may be found'
No relevant material.

Part 12. 'Remarks upon the Account the learned Dr Freind has given of an aneurism in his Hist. of Physick'

D129 'Observations on Dr Freind's acct of Aneurisms'. Part of some longer work for the first page is numbered 1 [6]
Unidentified handwriting. pp 20.

D130 Notes on writers on aneurisms, which do not relate directly to the scheme of the Treatise.
Amanuensis, James Parsons with additions by James Douglas. pp 97. [BT11.4]

Letters to James Douglas from:

D130.71 Wm Heathcote, St James's Square, 22 Aug 1737.

D130.77 J Hall, Warwick, Feb. 1736.
and an account with Mr Wm Bridgman, Painter 1725/6-1736

D130.70 Mr Lampard for size, 1736.
Mr Thos. Wilson two payments in 1730, and a further payment for a course of chemistry, 1731. These payments have been totalled by William Hunter.

D130a Aneurisms.
Fine manuscript in Greek. pp 2.

"A Remarkable Case of an Aneurism from the Memoires of the Royal Academy of Sciences by Dr James Douglas." 16 May 1728. (CP xii {ii} 40).

Miscellaneous notes on surgery

D131 Note on surgical instruments. p 1.

D132 Note on the extirpation of tonsils. p 1. [BT 18.4]

D133 Notes on writers on the veins in relation to venesection.
Amanuensis, James Parsons. pp 6.

D134 Surgical notes.
Writer not identified. pp 2.

D135 Notes on bandages.
Writers not identified. pp 3.

D136 '*De Herniis*'
Notes on transcription from an unidentified work in Latin on hernias.
In two unidentified hands. pp 12.

D137 Notes on various surgical authors, in same hand as part of D136. pp 14.

D138 'Of the removal of a large fungous execrescence from the *collum uteri* by help of a new sort of canula invented by Francis Sandys and Claudius Amyand Esqr Sergeant Surgeon to his Majesty' with a drawing of the instrument, 24 May 1739. pp 2.

D139 Drawings of surgical instruments unidentified. pp 5.

Materia Medica

D140 Notes on medicines and their uses, almost entirely in Latin, possibly notes from a lecture. pp 8.

D141 Prescriptions for various complaints, in English. pp 27.

D142 Prescriptions for various complaints. pp 16.

D143 Collection of prescriptions, mainly in James Douglas's hand, some dated between 1714 and 1724.
In unlabelled folder. pp 3. [BT 13.6]

D144 '*Pharmocop. St Thomae*'
A collection of prescriptions, partly in James Douglas's handwriting and partly in unidentified hand.
In a folder from a wrapping addressed:
"To Dr Douglas
at ye blew boar
against fetter lane
at an apothecary". pp 33. [BT 13.11]

D145 '*Medicamentorum quaedam formulae in praxi clariss DD Paul Chamberlen med: Doc: et practic: Londin: folicissim: magis familiares*'.
pp 26. [BT 13.5]

D146 '*Supplementum ad pharmae Londinensis*'
pp 4. [BT 18.ii 2]

D147 *Observationes* in D: Th: *praxi* and *Ext corti*: *Peruv*: by C. H.'
and one loose note.
Handwriting not identified, but it occurs again in MsH 484, *Incerti Auctoris Memoranda Medica*, and is very similar to that of Douglas's cousin Kennaway. pp 10. [BT 13.10]

D148 Prescriptions.

In James Douglas's handwriting written on the back of a document signed by P. Chamberlen and witnessed by Frances Walker, 13 Mar. 1708, relating to a bond of £400:

"conditional for the payment of two hundred pounds of like money unto Dr [?Chamberlen] ... entered into as above said the two condition where of is that if the said James [Douglas] shall be married to Captain Hoggs widow together with her fortune being possessed thereof then the said obligation to remain good in law otherwise the said bond to be void on the day specified in the bond vizt. the one and twentieth day of March in the year of our Lord one thousand seven hundred and nine witness my hand and soul this one and twentieth day of March 1708.
P Chamberlen."

D149 Seven letters to James Douglas giving him receipts for medicines.

i. "This is Dr Dover's secret and his apothecary Mr Fox in the strand obs this makes the patient very sick its operation is safe."

ii. "To Doctor Dugles at the Blew Bore an apothecary Shop near St Dunstans Church in Fleet Street, London.
Sir William Williams his family pill.
The incomparable pill by Sir W. W. etc."

iii. "A receipt for the gravel or stone."

iv. "O*rvietanum Romanum*, 1 Aug. 1724.
NB this is said to be that ovietam that Carnet or Tilburg expelled the poison with, all that he took before King Charles when he afterwards purchased the receipt at a very good price from the Dr."

v. "*La Boule Medicamen sense de Doctor Helvetius*."

vi. "Mr Drummond says the Fir Tree that is used in making chouden beer [A liquor made by boiling the black spruce in water and mixing molasses with the decoction. OED] ... an excellent antiscorbutic and pectorall."

vii. "Description of a drink called Bland, which is commonly used by the natives of Zetland."
[BT 13.3, 13.8, 16.8]

D150 "To make Dr Chamberlens Golden Mixture to promote quick and easy labour".
Unidentified handwriting. p 1. [BT 16.8]

D151 In a folder labelled by James Douglas 'Receipts Physical'
Slips with medical receipts, some initialled, in various handwritings. pp 11.

D152 Prescriptions from various medical men, i.e. Dr Lowers; Dr Anskine, 17 Jun. 1704; Gibbons, 14 Jan. 1695; Mr Trist, 1695; Dr Rudgly; Dr Brady in Cambridge; H. S.; Hans Sloane; Dr Cole; H. T.; T. S.; J. Ratcliffe; Drs Woodward; Bates; Salmon; Sutcliffe; M. France. pp 28. [BT 13.12, 13.14]

D153 A collection of receipts and prescriptions. pp 43. [BT 18.1]

D153a List of medicinal preparations.
Unidentified handwriting. p 14.

D154 Pinned into folder labelled by James Douglas '*Elix: pptis*'.
'*Elix: proprietatis helmiontis* with remarks'.

Instructions for making this medicine. pp 4. [BT 19.15]

D155 'Of the purging Salt', 28 July 1733.
Apparently James Douglas was thinking of selling up a chemical laboratory for the preparation of 'curious medicines' and suggested that Thomas Wilkins should co-operate on this project, taking a share of the profits. Wilkins was a chemist with his own laboratory, and suggested that at first he should work from his own premises till he could see if the project was viable. He was also concerned with salt mines in Hampshire, from which Purging Salt was prepared. He gives a description of the mines, the preparations of the salt, with a plan of the saltworks. pp 32. [BT 19.1]

D156 Notes on Sir Walter Raleigh's Cordial.
Extracts from Robert Boyle's *Some considerations touching the usefulness of experimental natural philosophy* (1663) and notes on other references to the cordial, its contents and uses.
Partly in James Douglas's hand, partly in Thomas Wilkins(?) hand.
Notes on the life of Sir Walter Raleigh, extracts from Robert Boyle's work and other references.
Modifications(?) of the receipt for particular diseases.
Amanuensis, G. Douglas. pp 20. [BT 19.8]

D157 '*Philonis Antidotis'*.
Amanuensis, G. Douglas. Post 1726, the date of publication of John Freind's *History of Physic*, which is mentioned. pp 25. [BT 19.9]

D158 Catalogue of prescriptions.
Amanuensis, Walter Tulideph. pp 26. [BT 19.16]

D159 List of authors whose writings have some implications for *materia medica*.
Arranged alphabetically from Hippocrates to Josephus Miller, 1722.
Amanuensis, W. Tulideph, additions and

corrections by James Douglas. pp 45 with numerous added slips.

D160 Notes in Latin and English on the nature and properties of various chemicals. pp 8.

D161 '*Annotationes Chymicae*', 28 Feb. 1702. Notes on the medical properties of various chemicals. pp 4.

D162 Notes in Latin and English on the preparations of various chemicals. pp 25.

D163 Notes on Mr Wilson's chemical activities.

George Wilson (1631-1711), lectured on Chemistry in London; see Gibbs, F. W., 'George Wilson', *Endeavour* **xii** (1953) 182-5.

D164 In a folder labelled by James Douglas 'Mr Walker' and in another hand 'Chemistry Botany *varia*'. The first page is headed

"These 50 new preparations with above 100 of the official ones shall all be faithfully prepared. To which will be added the chemical analysis of some of the vegetables most used in the practice of physic as opium, the cortex etc."

A few pages further on, in a different hand, "In all 182 whereof 53 are new".
Much of the material in note form. pp 55.

D165 In a folder labelled by James Douglas 'Oars' Notes on ores, minerals, mines and mining.

D166 Notes on how to build a furnace. pp 2.

D167 In a folder labelled by James Douglas '*Valeriana*' and 'The Chemical Analysis of Tobacco by J.D.' An account of the analysis, 26 July 1721, in unidentified hand, and a botanical description of *Nicotiana major* and *Nicotiana minor* by Walter Tulideph, additions by James Douglas. pp 8. [BT 19.3]

D168 Three copies in unidentified handwriting of experiments upon Shadwell water.
Second and third copies incomplete. pp 3. [BT 19.5]

D169 A letter, unsigned, London 16 Aug. 1716, presumably to James Douglas, about making a copper still, where to buy Cullycoat coal and other chemical directions. p 1.

D170 Notes on various chemical processes in the handwriting of D169, and a transcription of part in the handwriting of Kennaway. pp 6.

D171 Note on the preparation of a prescription.
Unknown hand. p 1.

D172 Notes on the preparation of various prescriptions.
Unknown hand. pp 7. [BT 19.13]

D173 Classification of parts of plants and animals according to their chemical and pharmacological properties.
In Latin. Transcription of part in unknown hand. pp 19.

D174 List of simple medicines arranged alphabetically.
Similar to those listed in James Douglas's *Index Materiae Medicae*, London (1724), but with no descriptions.
Unidentified hand, with additions and corrections by James Douglas. pp 10.

D175 Draft for James Douglas's *Index Materiae Medicae* (1724).
Not identical with printed version.
Same handwriting as D174, with corrections and additions by James Douglas. pp 23.

D176 Draft of *Index Materiae Medicae* (1724).
Not identical with printed version.
Unidentified hand, with additions and corrections by James Douglas. pp 31. [BT 19.14]

D177 Draft of *Index Materiae Medicae* (1724).
Not identical with printed version.

Unidentified handwriting, part similar to D176, part similar to D174 and D175, with additions and corrections by James Douglas. pp 76.

D178 Draft of *Index Materiae Medicae* (1724).
Not identical with printed version.
Unidentified hands, parts similar to D175, part to D176, with additions and corrections by James Douglas. pp 54.

D179 Draft of part of a table 'The simple medicines are reduced under general heads'.
p 101 in *Index Materiae Medicae* (1724).
Unidentified hand, similar to D176, with additions and corrections by James Douglas. pp 11.

D180 Descriptions of plants arranged alphabetically *Abies faemina* to *Absynthum vulg & Rom.*
Unidentified handwriting. pp 2.

D181 '*Agaricae*'
Notes on the tree fungus that grows on larches, used as a cathartic. pp 2. [BT 13.7]

D182 A letter from R. Middleton Massey to James Douglas, 4 Apr. 1724.
Sending a prescription and a list of his pharmacological books. pp 2.

D183 Slip.
Recto - notes on sena.
Verso - heading for a proposed work, possibly on sena.

D183a Bound collection of receipts for various kinds of medicine, with index.
In unidentified hand. pp 37.

'A lexicon for *Materia Medica*', with the Latin name, its Genitive case, Greek name, English name etc. MsH 542.
Handwriting of D175 and D176, with corrections and additions by James Douglas.

'Of Medicinal Plants'. MsH 552.
Amanuensis, G. Douglas.

'Materia Medica', vol I. MsH 612.
Handwriting of D170.

'Materia Medica', vol II. MsH 613.
Handwriting of D170, with additions by James Douglas

'Materia Medica'. MsH 614.
An alphabetical list of drugs, references to them by different authors, Douglas's own description of them, and their use by different doctors.

'Chemical potions made by my order at Mr Durhams Laboratory in Cheesewell Street, London 1725'. MsH 624.
Titles in James Douglas's hand, rest of Ms by Walter Tullideph.

'Prescriptions'. MsH 625.
From various sources in unidentified hand, with later additions and some slips with prescriptions in a different hand. The same as that of the Ms notes in *Pharmacopoeia Londiniensis* (1650). MsH 243.

'Catalogus Pharmacorum'. MsH 626.
Handwriting unidentified.

'Catalogus simplicum'. MsH 627.
Left hand column - Latin names of plants, in unidentified hand.
Right hand column - English names of plants by James Douglas.

'Of a certain bark called *Cortex Elatherii*, done into English from the French memoire of the Académie des Sciences by J. D.' Read, 8 Feb. 1721/22. (CP x {i} 44).

Medical Practice

James Douglas returned from the Continent in 1700 after having taken his medical degree at Rheims in 1699. He settled in London. About 1702 he became an assistant to Dr Paul Chamberlen and kept careful notes of his cases, often recording the opinion and advice of Chamberlen and also of Sir David Hamilton, Sir Hans Sloane, etc.

D184 Prescriptions and account of 2 cases, names of patients in Greek letters. 11 Jan. 1700. pp 2.

D185 15 cases with prescriptions. 3 May 1700-1703. pp 7.

D186 An account of James Douglas's treatment of himself, 12 Jan. 1700/01, also in D185.

D187 In folder labelled by James Douglas '*Casus* 1702-1703'.
Records of 47 cases between 10 Jan. 1702/3 and Feb. 1703/4.
Case 4 records the use of the forceps (*modo nostro*) in which the forceps bent and were useless. Dr Hamilton advised in cases 27 and 35, Dr P. C. (Chamberlen) advised in cases 37 and 47. pp 21.

D188 Pages 2-6 of a case history, written on wrapper of letter to Dr Chamberlen.
Though the account was written by Douglas, the case was probably in the care of Chamberlen. Dr Woodward and Dr Robinson also consulted. pp 8.

D189 Two case histories with queries as to appropriate treatment, and as to whether a man who kicked a pregnant women who subsequently died was guilty of murder, 28 Oct. pp 2.

D190 Case histories, mostly in Latin.
6 Jan. - Sept., no year. pp 4.

D191 Case histories, Mrs Wilkinson and Mr Pomrey.
Dec., no year. pp 3.

D192 Notes on various patients whom Douglas had seen possibly on behalf of Dr Chamberlen.
4 cases, 11 Sept.; 6 cases, 12 Sept. 1 folded sheet.

D193 "Captain Vincent's lady ... came for advice how she might prevent miscarrying." 29 Aug. 1704. p 1.

D194 In folder made from *Syllabus* of James Douglas's anatomy lectures, and labelled '*Abortio*'.

18 cases between 7 Sept. 1704 and 4 Nov. 1711. pp 38. [BT 13.1, 18.4]

D195 Prenatal complications.
2 cases, 25 Jan. 1710/11. pp 4.

D196 In a folder labelled '*Affectio hyster, conceptio hesa, cancer uteri, Procedentia uteri, tumor ovarii,Dolor inquine, haemorrhagia uteri*',
made from the *Syllabus* of James Douglas's anatomy lectures and an inner folder labelled '*Affectio hysterica*' made from *A Review of the British Nation,* 20 Jun. 1710.
4 cases of hysteria, 28 Aug. 1707 - 13 May 1709. pp 18. [BT 18.4]

D197 In folder labelled '*Procedentia uteri*' made from *Syllabus* of James Douglas's anatomy lectures.
8 cases, 23 Apr. 1707 - 13 Aug. 1711. pp 29. [BT 18.11.3]

D198 '*Tumour ovarii*'
3 cases, 18 Jun. 1705 - 18 Feb. 1707/8. pp 6.

D199 '*Dolor inquinalis*'
4 cases, 7 Oct. 1707 - 7 Sept. 1710. pp 12.

D200 '*haemorrhagia uteri et fluxus humour ...*'
20 cases, 17 Apr. 1704 - 11 Apr. 1711. pp 26.

D201 '*Cancer in utero*'
9 cases, 24 Apr. 1707 - 4 May 1711. pp 41. [BT18.11.3]

D202 '*Fluor albus*'
8 cases, 18 Aug. - 5 Dec. 1709. pp 20. [BT 18.4]

D203 '*Tumor labior pudenti*'
1 case, 18 Apr. 1711. p 1.

D204 Postnatal complications.
5 cases, 24 Oct. 1710 - 7 Jun. 1711. pp 6.

D205 Gynaecological cases.
6 cases, 26 Aug. 1704 - 4 Oct. 1708. pp 13.

D206 '*Hydrops ovari*'
2 cases, 29 Sept. 1705 - 27 Jan. 1710/11. pp 4. [BT 18.11.3]

D207 "Mrs Granger wanting 6 weeks of her time taken with pain." 19 July 1711.
Verso - letter to James Douglas from G. Wanchope, 18 July 1711. p 1. [BT 18.11.3]

D208 'Herpes'
"Benj Kennedy my cousin Kennedyes oldest son aged 14 ... " 25 Sept. 1710.

D209 Part of folder made from *Syllabus* of Douglas's anatomy lectures and labelled '*Dyarrhaea, vomitus, Dolor ventriculi et colicus*'.

D210 Labelled '*Dyarrhaea'*, folder covered by lists of numbers.
6 cases, 30 Aug. 1704 - 19 Sept. 1708. pp 15. [BT 18.4]

D211 '*Vomitio*'
11 cases of vomiting, 28 Aug. 1704 - 1 July 1711. pp 20.

D211. 4 Apr. 1707, 'Mrs North', with attached slip: "Mrs North Acct £4-0-0, attendance from April 15 - May the 15."

D212 '*Dolor ventricculi et colicus*'
9 cases, 19 July - 2 Mar. 1711. pp 23.

D213 Disorders of the digestive system.
3 cases, 15 Jun. 1704 - 18 Sept. 1710. pp 14. [BT 18.4]

D214 Folder made from *Syllabus* of Douglas's anatomy lectures and labelled '*Affectus renum et vesicae*'.
11 cases, 9 Dec. 1704 - 23 Nov. 1711. pp 31. [BT 18.4]

D214.26 Two views of the Stones taken out of Mrs Guypes kidneys.
Verso - drawing of male figure.

D215 'Dropsies'
4 cases, 10 July 1704 - 23 Mar. 1709, pp 5. [BT 18.4]

D216 '*Palpitatio cordis*'
1 case, 14 Jan. 1708. pp 2.

D217 '*Rubor faciaei*'
9 Mar. 1709. pp 2 [BT 18.4]

D218 A description of Bell's Palsy.
18 Aug. 1704. p 1.

D219 Disorders of the Eyes
7 cases, 30 Mar. 1704 - 15 Oct. 1710. pp 10.

D220 '*Chlorosis*'
1 case. pp 2. [BT 18.4]

D221 Folder made from a postscript to the *Daily Courant,* no. 2010, 30 July 1708, and labelled '*Affectus Pectores et pulmonum*'.
5 cases, 27 Jan. 1704 - 2 Mar. 1711. pp 7. [BT 18.4]

D222 '*Inflam Tonsillarii*'
2 cases, 4 Oct. 1708. pp 3. [BT 18.4]

D223 '*Icterus et nephritis*'
2 cases, 2 May 1707 - 5 Aug. 1710. pp 3.

D224 '*Salivato*'
2 cases, 27 Feb. 1704 - 2 Oct. 1711. pp 11.

D225 'Scrophula'
1 case, 28 Feb. 1711. p 1. [BT 18.ii.3]

D226 'Scabies'
1 case, 13 May 1705. pp 2. [BT 18.4]

D227 '*Dolor dentis*'
1 case, 3 Jan. 1706. p 1.

D228 '*Contusio mamillae*'
2 cases, 15 Mar. 1703/4. p 1.

D229 Bone injuries
4 cases, 8 Feb. 1709 - 2 Nov. 1711. pp 8.

D230 In folder made from *Syllabus* of Douglas's anatomy lectures, folded, one half labelled '*Febris*' and the other '*Insuelus epilept: Febris, Gonorrhea, Lues venerea*'.
19 cases, 6 Jan. 1705 - 21 Feb. 1711. pp 48. [BT 18.4]

D231 '*Variola*'
8 cases, 14 Dec. 1706 - 2 Feb. 1710/11. pp 3. [BT 18.4]

D232 '*Gonorrhoea*'
The case of Lieut Crosby, 18 Mar. 1706/7, with draft of a letter from Douglas to Crosby, and draft of a letter to unknown correspondent. pp 29. [BT 15.6]

D223 '*Gonorrhoea*'
9 cases, 28 Mar. 1708 - 3 Mar. 1710. pp 26. [BT 18.ii.3]

D234 '*Lues venera*'
4 cases, 20 Sept. 1707 - 23 Mar. 1710. pp 17.

D235 '*Insuelus epilectic and Motus convulsivi*'
3 cases, 20 Sept. 1704 - 24 Mar. 1709. pp 3.

D236 '*Passio hypochondriaca*'
3 cases, 19 Sept. 1709 - 5 Feb. 1710. pp 3.

D237 '*Apoplexia*'
1 case, 17 Sept. 1710. p 1.

D238 '*Dolor capitis*'
1 case, 25 Nov. 1710. p 1.

D239 Miscellaneous cases
- i. Mrs Rhodes' cousin, 22 Dec.
- ii. "Mrs Rhodes' girl that I laid her of ... "
- iii. Mrs Kingsman.
  Verso - letter from James Houston.
- iv. Mr - , 3 Sept. 1711.
- v. S. Eastham a weaver [BT 18.6]
- vi. "... she had a very severe looseness ..."
- vii. "... about eleven she expired."

viii. Notes in Latin. 2 Apr. 1706. "A girl aged about 12 year ... complained of a pain in her right side."

ix. "A violent pain in the stom: and belly."

D240 A list of questions asked or to be asked of a patient. p 1.

D241 A prescriptions for patients. 6 Jan. 1701 - 13 Jan. 1711/12. pp. 4.

D241.1 On part of an invitation to a Ball, 8 Apr. 1701, at Ye Consort Room Viller's Street given by Walter Holt(?).

After 1711 there are very few detailed case histories, possibly because Douglas had ceased to be assistant to Paul Chamberlen and had established his own practice.

D242 Mrs Rand, 25 Aug. 1721.

D243 Prescriptions for named patients, arranged alphabetically. 7 Mar. 1714/15 - 24 Oct. 1741. [BT.18.11]

D242.3 with dissection notes, 24 Oct. 1715.

D242.64 Notes on Augustus Caesar, unidentified hand.

Amongst his patients were:-
Various members of his wife's family, the Wilkes; the Hon. Lady How; Mrs Walpole, Master Walpole (the family of Horatio Walpole, younger brother of Sir Robert Walpole); The Countess of Lippe; the Rt. Hon. the Lady Percival; the Hon. Miss Conway; the Hon. the Countess Gillenborg; Lady Smyth; Lady Rich; the Hon. Mrs Vernon, the Hon. Lady Beddingfield, Lady Russell, Miss Sarah Papillon, the Hon. Mrs Rolt, Lord Drumlanrig. pp 99.

D244 Prescriptions without patients' names. pp 20.

D244.8 Letter to James Douglas from M. P. Long.

Prescriptions by other physicians

D245 Prescription for the Rt. Hon. The Marquis of Lothian, 11 Feb. 1711 - 1 Mar., signed J. Arbuthnot. pp 2.

D246 For Mrs Dennis, 22 and 28 Feb. 1722, signed J. Fr. [?John Freind]

D247 Madame Bulstrode from Dr Beale. 20 Aug. 1718 - 13 Apr. 1722.

D248 Prescription for Mrs Hatley, 10 Apr. 1722, unsigned.

D249 Prescription for Mrs Middleton from Sir David Hamilton, 26 Dec. 1719.

D250 5 prescriptions for "Mrs Buckley at Mr Chapman's over against St Clement's Church", signed C.P.S. [?Conrad Joachim Spiengell] 25 Oct. to 14 Nov.

D251 For Master Wilks, 21 Sept. 1723, signed W. or T.V.

D252 "The powders for Mrs Walpole", 28 Sept. 1723, signed G. C.

D253 2 prescriptions for Master Wymondsel (or Wimondsold), one signed G. C., the other JB or S.B., 31 July 1724.

D254 13 prescriptions for Mrs Wise, 1723-1724, signed JB

D255 Prescription for Mrs Webb, 20 Sept. 1725, unsigned.

D256 Prescription for Madam Styles, 16 Feb., unsigned.

D257 Prescription for Master Long, undated, unsigned. D255, 256 and 257 appear to be in the same handwriting.

D258 Prescriptions for Madam Hillersden (at Mr Jenks added by Douglas) 24 Feb. 1725, unsigned.

D259 Prescriptions for the Lady Arabella Denny, 28 Sept. - 4 Oct. 1726, unsigned.

D260 4 prescriptions for Mrs Baddison. 3 July-13 July 1726. Signed JBB. or A.B.B. [?Arnold Boot Beirman]

D261 Addressed to James Douglas.
Prescriptions for Madam Booth, 18 Jan. 1727/8 "These are prescriptions copy'd exactly from Dr Freind
I am Sir
yr very humble servt
Wm. Tomlinson."

D262 2 prescriptions for Mrs Kennedy, 20 and 21 Sept. 1728, unsigned.

D263 A copy of Dr Holling's prescriptions for the Rt Hon. Lady Conway, 19 Nov. 1729 - 31 July 1730.

D264 Prescriptions for Mrs Webber from Dr Brooke, 7 Feb. - 16 Mar. 1730/31.

D265 Prescriptions for Madam Gordon, 14 Sept. 1740, unsigned.

D266 Prescriptions for the Rt. Hon. Lady Fairfax, 16 Feb. 1739/40 - 2 May 1740, signed C.W. These were sent in a letter addressed to Mrs Cholmely by Gran. Bredall which "you are to lett ye Doctors have".

D267 Prescription for Mrs Goodall, undated, unsigned.

D268 Prescriptions for Madam Martin, 'The copy of the Drs Prescriptions', undated, unsigned.

D269 Prescription for Mrs Broo[k?], 20 Jan., signature cut away.

D270 Prescription for (?) Mrs Bing, 4 Nov. signed D. H. [?David Hamilton] and JB

D271 Prescription - unsigned - against which James Douglas has written 'Sir Edmund King'.

D272 Headed 'Dr Bamber', 4 prescriptions.

D273 7 pages of prescription in different hands, no patients.

D274 Relocated.

Post Mortems

D275 17 Dec. 1703, *Londini.*
"Mr Sutcliff my landlord had a child opened this day by Mr Martin a young surgeon". The child had suffered a series of accidents. [BT 18.6]

D276 18 Nov. 1715.
"I opened a woman at Islington of about 50 years of age that never had a child ..."
Pathological condition of the urino-genital system.
Written on the draft of a letter by James Douglas about a warrant.

D227 12 Mar.
'An observation of two perfect teeth found in the right ovarium of a woman' by J. D.
Draft of a paper read to the Royal Society (JB xii p 448). [BT 5.14]

D278 "Upon opening the body of Pitfeild who died 1741/2 aged - I observed a great stagnation of blood in all the vessels of the *pia mater* ..."

Miscellaneous Medical Papers

D279 '*Index Morborum, Anno 1707*' and '*Index Morborum, Anno 1708*' (Jan. only) pp 4 [BT 18.ii.4]

D280 On the 'vapours' in men and women. [BT 18.4]

D281 Etmuller on the treatment of *Fluor alb.*

D282 Part only of notes in Latin on some medical text with comments in English. pp 9.

D283 Notes on the mode of operation of purgatives. p 1.

D284 Notes on diseases and their treatment. pp 20.

D285 Notes on Gonorrhoea. pp 5.

D286 Notes on '*pas: hypochondr*'. p 1.
Verso - letter to James Douglas from M. King.

D287 Note on diseases of bones. p 2.

D288 Notes on '*Opthalmia epiphora*'. pp 5. [BT 18.1]

Letters to James Douglas from:

D288.3 Verso - fragment from Arch. Douglas, 11 Oct. 1708.

D288.4 Fragment of legal document concerning loan of £30 to Mr King. (See D286 verso.)

D289 Notes on *variola*. pp 3 [BT 18.1]

D290 Notes on Paralysis. pp 2.

D291 Notes on *Lethargia*. pp 3.

D292 Notes on *Calentura*. p 1.

D293 Notes on Colick. p 1.

D294 Notes on *Fistula in ano*. pp. 5.

D295 Notes on Fevers. p 1 [BT 13.12]

D296 Notes on the Toothach. p 1.

D297 Latin definitions of diseases. pp. 8.

D298 Notes in Latin on unidentified work on the fontanelles in an infant. pp 34 [BT 9.5]

D299 Notes on tonsils and diseases of the throat. p 1.

D300 Notes in Latin on Galen's *Compositione medicamentorum*. p 1.

D301 Notes from Bellini on malignant and pestilential fevers. pp 2.

D302 "Opening the jugulars in dis: of the head ...". p 1.

D303 "Continual vomiting may proceed according to p:c: [Paul Chamberlen] ..." p 1.

D304 'Mr Couper' [?Cowper]
Report on his practice. pp 2.

D305 "I could see the iris as through as cloud". p 1.

D306 Notes on unidentified subjects. pp 3.

Letter to James Douglas from:
D306.1 H Figuel, 19 Jan. 1713/14.

D307 Notes on Celsus on bites of mad dogs.
Amanuensis, G. Douglas. pp 4.

D308 Notes on [Aetius] *De Notis Pulsib.* cap xxvii.
Unidentified hand. p 1. [BT 25.1]

D309 'Dr parrie'
Charles Parry (?), 1698-1780, author of various works on mineral water. However this article on the drinking of mineral waters refers to "a purging water ... at Ashford near Castle Cary ... discovered by Thomas Earle (?), minister of that place and communicated to me in the year 1670 by letter".
And
"Sir Thomas Brown[e] of Norwich [died 1682] my worthy, Good friend, with whom I had the honour to correspond by letters ..." pp 33. [BT 11.4]

Lecture Notes

The following manuscripts are probably notes taken by James Douglas, or by James and possibly his brother John, of lectures they attended. Nowhere is the name of the lecturer given. Notes in Latin may date from James's time in Utrecht, those in French suggest attendance at lectures in Paris. James obtained his medical degree from Rheims and may have attended lectures there.

D310 A set of notes of anatomy lectures in sections A-Z in Latin with comments in Latin and French.
Refers to Du Verney's opinions. pp 138. [BT 6.8]

D311 '*Osteologia*'
Notes in English on anatomy lectures, section 2-5 missing.
Partly in James Douglas's hand, partly in a different hand that might be that of John Douglas. Contains much comparative anatomy. Dealing with the comparative anatomy of the stomach, the names given to the different parts in a ruminant are given in French, suggesting a French lecturer,

possibly G. J. Duverney who was very interested in comparative anatomy. Also reference to a "boy in Paris who never could abstaine from rumination tho' frequently whipt for it". pp 71. [BT 9.6]

While there is no evidence that James Douglas gave anatomy lectures before 1706, the following notes read like notes for his own lectures, but they may be notes of lectures Douglas attended at the Barber Surgeons' company.

D312 '*Osteologia*'
Brief descriptions of bones. 1704 - dated on the last page. pp 16.

D313 '*Pericordia*'
Notes with extensive comments. Finish 1 Dec. 1704 (last page). While the notes almost certainly are by James Douglas, the comments also by James Douglas show a slight change in handwriting and suggest the comments were added some time later.

D314 '*Auris* etc.'
Notes on the ear, brain and cranial nerves, ending with 'Mr Rolfes method of dissecting the brain 2 Aug. 1704'.
And
"This account of ye origination of the nerves fro the med: obl: I took from the brain of a woman I had from Tyburn in y month of Mar. 1705."
Plus loose notes on the brain.
In multi-coloured folder. pp 46.

D315 '*Neurologia*'
On the cranial and spinal nerves. pp 16.

D316 Notes of a lecture on the eye. pp 2.

D315 Latin descriptions of diseases and their treatment with case histories and occasional comments in English and French dating from 1702-1703. pp 90. [BT 18.5]

D318 Fragment of notes in Latin. p 1.

D319 Notes in French on complications of pregnancy and their treatment, with comments in English. pp 4.

D320 Notes on diseases of the female reproductive system with an Index to an extensive work on pregnancy, of which the notes form part.
This may be a draft for Douglas's projected work on the diseases of women, see DF53. pp 10.

The Rabbit Woman of Godalming

In 1726 James Douglas became involved in the case of Mary Toft, the Rabbit Woman of Godalming, who claimed to have given birth to rabbits.

D321 A letter from William Pountney at Farnham to his father in Kensington, undated, giving an account of events in Godalming relating to Mary Toft. His letter was circulated to various people including "ye Dcts". pp 2 and contemporary engraving of the events. [BT 20.7]

D322 Letter from St André telling Douglas that Mary Toft has been brought from Guildford to the Bagnio in Leicester Fields, 29 Nov. 1726. [BT 20.7]

D323 Letter from St André to James Douglas. 3 Dec. 1726.
St André attempts to persuade Douglas to continue an interest in the case. [BT 20.11]

D324 Mary Toft's confession on 7 Sept., taken down by James Douglas. In this confession she accuses the wife of the organ-grinder for putting her up to the deception. pp 15.

D325 Fair copy of Mary Toft's confession.
Amanuensis, (?)G. Douglas. pp 6. [BT 20.5, 20.6]

D326 An account of Mary Toft's first confession.
Amanuensis, (?)G. Douglas. pp 2.

D327 Mary Toft's confession on 8 Dec. taken down by James Douglas. In this she implicates her mother-in-law and Mr Howard, the Guildford surgeon. pp 12. [BT 20.5]

D328 Mary Toft's confession on 12 Dec., taken down by James Douglas in which she implicates her mother-in-law. pp 4.

D329 Recto - Statement of why James Douglas cannot publish an account of Mary Toft's confession. Amanuensis, (?)G. Douglas.
Verso - A restatement of why Douglas cannot publish the confession. In unidentified hand. p 1.

D330 Draft of James Douglas's *Advertisement occasioned by some passages in Sir R Manningham's diary lately published*, London (1727), including six attempts at the introduction. pp 34. [BT 20.10; 20.12]

D331 Statement in unknown hand that James Douglas believed in the rabbit-births and that Manningham and Douglas, together with St André and Howard, were in league over the deception. p 1.

D332 Transcribed extract from *Whitehall Evening Post*, 29 Dec. 1726. Headings in Douglas's hand, extract in unidentified hand. p 1. [BT 20.2]

D333 Transcribed extract from *Daily Journal* and from *Daily Post*, 9 Jan. 1727, on prosecution of Mary Toft and Mr Howard. p 1. [BT 20.3]

D334 Notes on authors' accounts of monstrous births, and comments on authors who wrote on the case of Mary Toft.
Amanuensis, G. Douglas. pp 24. [BT 20.2, 20.9]

D335 A list of parts of rabbit, presumably those removed from Mary Toft. p 1.
Verso - letter to James Douglas from W. Kinleside, ND.

D336 Two copies of John Arbuthnot's *Bunny's Dad*. One by James Douglas; the other in an unidentified hand. pp 2. [BT 20.4]

D337 *A full and true account of a Horrid, Cruel, Barbarous, Bloody and Inhuman Self Murder committed by Ann Toft.* 27 Dec.
Purporting to be an account of the suicide of [Mary] Toft. Full of errors. Mary Toft's husband was Joseph, not William. Mary Toft died in 1763. See *The Gazetteer*, 21 Jan. 1763.

There is a card-index bibliography of publications relating to Mary Toft.

James Douglas and the Princess of Orange

James Douglas, as Physician in Extra-Ordinary to Queen Caroline, became concerned with the health of Princess Anne, the Princess Royal, eldest daughter of George II and Queen Caroline, who married the Prince of Orange in London on 14 March 1734. She went with the Prince to Holland in April but returned to England on 29 June while he was with the army. Crossing back to Holland on 6 November she was taken ill and was brought back to Harwich. As she was believed to be pregnant James Douglas, and the former midwife to Queen Caroline, Mrs Mairbom, were sent to look after her. James Douglas wrote to the Prince of Orange saying that in her condition he thought it would be dangerous for the Princess to make the sea-crossing to Holland. Her father insisted on her returning to her husband. She left in December, accompanied by Mrs Mairbom and Dr G. L. Tessier, Physician in Ordinary to George II, who took over organising mid-wifery support for the Princess. Whether James Douglas was also in attendance is not known but he certainly was in Holland at the beginning of 1735.

Although the Princess became fat it was now doubted if she was pregnant. Ordered by Queen Caroline to confirm that she was pregnant, Douglas was not permitted to examine her, so could not give a definite answer, but finally it was accepted that she was not pregnant and he returned home. In April the Queen settled £500 per annum on him for his attendance on the Princess.

Apparently the Princess had taken a dislike to James Douglas and when she became pregnant in 1736 she was not attended by him. She gave birth to a dead child.

When she was again pregnant in 1739, those suggested by Tessier to attend the Princess did not meet with approval or declined to serve so that in the end the Princess was forced to accept James Douglas. Therefore Douglas again went to Holland. On 10 December the Princess gave birth to a daughter who lived only half an hour. Manuscripts relating to Douglas's attendance on the Princess of Orange are in the Dutch Royal Archives at the Hague.

Botany

James Douglas showed no interest in botany till 1718 when he gave papers to the Royal Society on mistletoe. The development of this interest may have coincided with the removal from Fetter Lane, where he could not have had a garden, to Bow Lane. Here many houses had gardens, but work on mistletoe did not necessitate a garden of his own. Most of his botanical work was done on plants of medicinal use.

Mistletoe

"Dr Douglas brought before the Society several branches of the mistletoe with its berry and seed." (JB, 8 Jan. 1718/19).

D338 In a wrapper made from a page from *Mists Journal* and labelled '*Propogandi modus*', 14 Jan. 1718/19. A short account of the different opinions about the vegetation of the *viscum* or mistletoe by J. D. pp 21. [BT 2.6]

Letter to James Douglas from:
D238.21 Deborah Reynolds.

D339 In a wrapper made from *The Weekly Journal or Saturday Post*, 3 Jan. 1719, and labelled '*Botanici*'. A Botanical Description of the plant called *viscum* or misseltoe by J. D., "I thought it not unseasonable entertainment to show this plant in all its parts before the gentlemen of this Society."

'Of the Differences in the *Viscum Arborem* and of its flowers by J. D.', 19 Feb. 1718/19.

"Dr Douglas produced several branches of different sorts of mistletoe" (JB, 19 Feb.).

The description of the *Viscum* continued by J D, 19 Mar. Two articles with similar titles. [BT 2.5]

D340 '*Analysis chymica*', 3 Mar. 1719, 27 Mar. 1719, [mistletoe] from the lime tree, and account of the expenses of the analysis.

"Dr Douglas gave a further description of the mistletoe with a chemical analysis." (JB, 12 Mar.).

D341 '*Composita*'
Notes on preparations of mistletoe from various authors. pp 4.

D342 In a folder made from a catalogue of books and labelled 'Read'.
'Observations on the growth of the *Viscum*'.
Dated observations on the growth of mistletoe, 2 Feb. - 20 Jun. 1719. pp 10.

D343 Notes on the structure of the mistletoe plant.

Letter to James Douglas from:
D343.1 John Douglas, ND. pp. 2.

D344 '*Delectus*'
Notes on the relative properties of mistletoe from different trees. pp 2.

D345 '*Arbores in quibus in nascitur et locus natatis*'
Notes on authors' opinions on the trees on which mistletoe grows. pp 4.

D346 Draft of letter relating to mistletoe growing on an oaktree five miles from Wolverhampton, 26 Mar. 1718.

D347 List of trees on which mistletoe grows.

Letter to James Douglas from Patrick Blair, re mistletoe including verso - list of trees on which mistletoe grow, from a letter from Mr Willisel to John Ray, to which James Douglas has added notes. pp 3 [BT 2.2].

D348 Sheet headed '*Aves visci vorae*', but no notes.

D349 '*Tempus quo floret et colligi debet*'
Notes on authors on the flowering and gathering of mistletoe. p 1.

D350 '*Partes officinales et modus operandi*'
Notes from various authors. p 1.

D351 '*Usus visci internus ae operandi modus*'
Notes on the uses of mistletoe. pp 11.

Letter to James Douglas from:
D351.8 John Thornycroft, 27 Feb. 1718.

D352 '*Etimologia*'
Notes on names for mistletoe in various languages and at different times. Several slips on the names and their derivations, signed Dr Jones, possibly David Jones (1676-1720), see DNB. pp 15.

D352.12 Partial key to Anglo Saxon alphabet.

James Douglas contemplated publishing an extensive work on mistletoe, see Patrick Blair, *Botanic Essays* (1720).

D353 Scheme of proposed work on mistletoe and rough draft. pp 6.

D354 Part of further draft for work on mistletoe. pp 14.

D355 In folder made from sheet of *Mists Journal* and labelled '*Autores citati*'.
Notes on authors on mistletoe.
Amanuensis, G. Douglas. pp 25. [BT 2.7]

D355.1 Verso - prescription for Mrs Lowlock, 29 May 1718.

Letters to James Douglas from:

D355.5 Thomas Howard, Guildford, 1 Jan. 1718.
D355.9 William Welsh, ND.
D355.20 Walter Douglas, 6 Apr. 1717.
D355.21 On back of *Cambridge Almanack* 1718

D356 List of authors on *Viscum.*
In folder made from *Parker's London News,* 30 Mar. 1719. pp 14.

D357 List of authors on *Viscum* arranged chronologically. pp 2.

D358 Articles on parasitical vegetables [by Patrick Blair] pp 4.

D359 '*Viscus Quercus*'
Information about mistletoe in Latin in unidentified hand, with notes by James Douglas. pp 4.

D360 '*De Visco Druidum*'
Dissertatio ad Noblissimum atq. Doctissimum Jac: Douglas MD by John Georgius Keysler [1689-1743, born Thurnau, traveller and antiquarian, FRS] pp 12.

D361 In wrapper made from sheet of notes on medical subject, by William George Douglas, labelled '*folia visci*'.
11 leaves of mistletoe. [BT 2.3]

D362 19 drawings in charcoal and white chalk on grey paper, of mistletoe, one signed P. R. Fremont 1718, with pencilled identification - possibly by Professor Young, Professor of Natural History 1866-1902.
In grey paper folder.

D362.6 Verso - Notes by James Douglas.

"A description of the virtues and use of a certain Bark called in French *Chacril* and in Latin *Cortex*

Elatherrii by James Douglas". Read 8 Feb. 1721/22. (CP x {i} 44).

Wild Valerian

D362a Note on 'Mr Rand's little valerian'. 14 Apr. 1722. Verso - fragment of legal agreement between James Douglas and Dr John Gardner in the reign of Queen Anne.

There is no other material relating to Douglas's paper to the Royal Society, 24 May 1722, on the Wild Valerian (JB). His discovery, in company with John Wilmer, of this plant on a common in Ilford is referred to in Dilleneus's edition of John Ray's *Synopsis Methodica* (1725). The manuscript of the paper (CP x {i} 47).

Crocus

D363 In a folder labelled '*Crocologia*'.
Notes on the structure of the saffron crocus.
Mainly in Walter Tullideph's hand, with additions by James Douglas. pp 24. [BT 8.1]

Letter to James Douglas from:
D363.17 John Corrie, 30 Dec. 1724.

D364 Notes on the Saffron crocus, one section dated 5 Oct. 1723.
Partly in Walter Tullideph's hand, with additions by James Douglas. pp 34.

D365 Notes on authors who have written on saffron crocus.
In the hands of Walter Tullideph, James Douglas and George Douglas. pp 69.

D366 Notes on saffron crocus from the works of Thomas Johnson, Caspar Bauhin, G. Ruff, H. Lyte and William Turner.
Unidentified hand, with additional notes by James Douglas. pp 16.

D367 *'Index Authorum Historicus'*
'Index Authorum Chronologicus'

'Index Authorum Alphiabeticus'
Drafts of indices with biographical notes on authors.
Amanuensis, G. Douglas. pp 38.

D368 Draft for 'Historical Account of Writers on Saffron'.
Some pages missing. pp 105.

An historical account of the Writers upon Saffron. MsH 600.

D369 Part of draft for 'Of Saffron'. MsH 588.
Amanuensis, G. Douglas, with addition by James Douglas. pp 67.

D370 'The Botanical Anatomy or Dissection of the plant called *Crocus Autumnalis*, that bears the true English Saffron with figures by James Douglas, Honorary Fellow of the Royal College of Physicians, and Fellow of the Royal Society'. 23 Oct. 1723.
Part of draft for Of Saffron. MsH 588.
No description of the figures is given but the figures are probably those in D375.
Amanuensis, G. Douglas, with additions by James Douglas. pp 67.

'Of Saffron' MsH 588.

'A Botanical Description of the Flower and Seed vessel of the plant called *Crocus Autumnalis sativus* that produces the true English Saffron of the shops' by James Douglas, 23 Oct. 1723. (CP x {ii} i). Published *Phil. Trans.* **xxxii** (1723) 441.

D371 Off-print of 'A Botanical Description ... ' from *Phil. Trans.* **xxxii**.

D372 Draft of a paper to the Royal Society comparing crocus corms with various bulbs.
Includes a statement "I have annexed a short Latin description of the True Saffron". This must be '*Croci sativi florantis crocus que*'.
In a folder made from *The British Journal*, 13 Jan.

1727/28.
Amanuensis, G. Douglas. pp 8.

"Of the root of the Crocus autumnalis". (JB, 25 Mar. 1725).

D373 Notes and observations on the growth of saffron crocus. 15 Sept. 1724 - 15 Sept. 1726. pp 14.

Letter to James Douglas from:
D373.5 Bernard Baron.
D373.7 St André.
D273.9 Joseph Harris, 8 Aug. 1725.
D373.11 Alex Burne, 27 July 1725, re Lord Drumlanrig's health.
D373.14 Arthur Sparkes, 6 Apr. 1726.

"An account of the culture and management of Saffron in England by James Douglas", 7 Nov. 1728. (CP x {ii} 9). Published in *Phil Trans* **xxxv** (1728) 566.

D374 Letters to James Douglas about Saffron:
i. "Take a pint of milk and boil it, then take Saffron ... ", unsigned, ND.
ii. Jos Malyn, 26 Oct. 1724.
iii. "Carthams(?) *crocus ortolamus* Saffron of ye garden", unsigned, ND.
iv. Mr Bradley on saffron, 18 Nov. 1727.
v. Philip Miller, 16 Dec. 1723.
vi. Philip Miller, 5 Mar. 1726/27.

D375 Drafts of descriptions of four '*composite tabulae*' of figures of saffron crocus. Probably the figures that should have been associated with D370. Descriptions in Walter Tullideph's hand, with additions by James Douglas.
Plans for the four *tabulae*, together with the finished drawings, in pen and wash, artist unknown. pp 23.
Drawings missing:- *Tab II* figs 3, 4, 5, 6, 7 (sketches for these figures probably in D376.3); *Tab III* fig 2; *Tab IV* figs 5 and 6.

Tab III fig 4 is reproduced in *Phil. Trans.* **xxxii** to illustrate Douglas's paper.

D376 Sketches, finished drawings in pen and ink of saffron crocus, and descriptions by James Douglas, 30 and 31 Jan. 1724. pp 7. [BT 8.2]

D377 Drawing 'Two roots [of saffron crocus] that grew in pots upon my own leads' p 1.

D378 Description of figures, sketches and finished drawings of two roots [of saffron crocus] from Chelsea Garden. 2 Jan. 1723/4.

D379 Undescribed sketches and finished pen and wash drawings of saffron crocus.

D380 Charcoal drawings of saffron crocus.
Artist possibly P.R. Fremont.

D381 Drawings in red chalk of saffron crocus, numbered and described by James Douglas. 14 Sept. 1726.
Artist unknown. pp 14.

D382 3 red chalk drawings of saffron crocus from near Saffron Walden, 18 Sept., descriptions by James Douglas.

D383 2 red chalk drawings of Saffron Crocus, dated May 1727, descriptions by James Douglas. In a plain folder. pp 2.

D384 2 red chalk drawings of saffron crocus, dated 5 Sept. 1728, descriptions by James Douglas. p 1.

D385 In folder labelled '*figurae croci*'.
3 red chalk drawings of saffron crocus, descriptions by James Douglas. pp 3.

D386 In folder labelled '*Crocus*'.
30 red chalk drawings of saffron crocus, no descriptions. [BT 8.1]

D387 A series of red chalk drawings of saffron crocus, mainly the corms.
Pinned onto 4 sheets, two of which are proof plates from the 'Osteology'.

The Guernsey Lily (*Nerine sarniensis*)

D388 Notes on authors who described plants which may or may not have been the Guernsey lily. Amanuensis, G. Douglas, with notes by James Douglas. pp 19.

D389 Plans and notes for a work on the Guernsey lily. pp 6.

D390 In a double folder, the outer labelled 'The Guernsay lilly', the inner made from two double pages of *Proposal for printing by Subscription a translation of the Seven Tragedies of Aeschylio by Mr Theobald* and pages of *Prometheus Chained.* '*Narcisso = Liron Sarniensis* or the Guernsay Lily Botanically described by J. D. 20 Oct. 1724, read before the [Royal] Society, 22 Oct. 1724'. Amanuensis, G. Douglas, with additions by James Douglas. pp 42.

"Dr Douglas communicated a discourse in Latin on the *Lirio-Narcissus* or Guernsay Lilly and abstract of a Discourse in English on the same subject lately communicated to the Society." (JB., 10 Dec. 1724).

D391 Observation on the growth of the Guernsey Lily from 19 July - 4 Oct. 1725, and 'Memorandum, 16 June 1726', attached to note on bulbs that flowered in October and describing dissection of bulb that flowered 'last October'.
In a folder made from *Proposals for printing by subscription Dr Englebert Kaempfer's Travels into Muscovy, Persia and the East Indies.* pp 10.

Letters to James Douglas from:
D391.1 Jean Albin, 2 July 1725.
D391.4 Geo. Finch, ND.
D391.5 W. Matthews, ND.
D391.6 J. Green, 29 June.
D391.10 Mary Taylor, ND.

D392 Observations on the growth of the Guernsey lily, 20 June - 30 Sept. 1726, and 21 Aug. - 17 Sept.

Published in *A Description of the Guernsey Lilly* (1729). In folder from cover of letter to James Douglas. pp 18.

D392.2 Prescription for Master Walpole, 4 Jun. 1726.
D392.15 Prescription for Mrs Apprice, ND.

Letters to James Douglas from:
D392.10 Arabella Williams, ND.
D392.12 Anna Du Roy, ND.

D393 In grey folder labelled '*Lilium Sarniensis*'. Observations on the growth of the Guernsey lily, 12 Aug. - 21 Sept. 1736. pp 6.

D394 Part of draft of first edition of *Lilium Sarniense: or a description of the Guernsay-Lilly* (1725). Including material not published. pp 23.

D395 Part of draft for the second edition, 1729. Amanuensis, G. Douglas. pp 21.

D396 Correspondence relating to the Guernsay Lily:

i. Letter from William Mathews, ND, sending an account of the Guernsey lily borrowed by Matthews for James Douglas, with what presumably is a transcription of the account by G. Douglas.

ii. Letter from Patrick Blair, unsigned, ND.

iii. Letter from J. G. Scheuchzer, 30 June 1726, together with Dr Kaempfer's description of the Guernsey lily.

iv. An account of the Guernsey lily, unsigned, dated 11 Dec. 1725, sent in response to an enquiry by James Douglas.

v. A reply, unsigned, to questions asked by James Douglas about the Guernsey lily.

vi. 2 letters, one a fragment only, the other dated 3 Nov. 1724, to Mr Rokeby in Hatton Garden from - de Beauvoir giving information about the Guernsay lilly.

vii. Information about the Guernsey lily and comments on Richard Bradley's *New Improvements of Planting and Gardening (1717).* Unsigned, undated. pp 16.

D397 Thomas Knoulton's diary of his visit to Guernsey on behalf of James Douglas to enquire into the history and cultivation of the Guernsay lily.
Brief notes on the geography of Guernsey and an account of the expenses of the visit.

D398 Letter to James Douglas from Thomas Knowlton from Buckingham House, 30 June 1726.

D399 Original drawings for *Tab I, Description of the Guernsey Lilly,* 1737. Missing figs 5, 6, 13, 20. The original drawings for *Tab II* in the 1725 edition and for *Tab III* have not survived.

D400 12 charcoal drawings of the Guernsey lily, possibly by P. R. Fremont.
In grey paper folder.

D401 4 pencil drawings of the Guernsey lily, numbered 1, 2, 4, 5, but no list of drawings corresponds with them. Artist unknown.

D402 12 red chalk drawings of bulbs of Guernsey lily. Artist unknown.

D403 8 red chalk drawings of dissected bulbs of Guernsay lily, showing embryo flower shoot. Possibly same artist as D382. Numbered in red chalk and pencil.
A page of descriptions by James Douglas that correspond with the pencil numbering.
2 red chalk drawings, with descriptions by James Douglas.
1 page describing drawing with which no drawing can be associated.

D404 9 red chalk drawings of dissected bulbs of Guernsay lily, proving that bulbs could flower more than once, numbered in pencil on verso. No descriptions correspond with these drawings.

D405 8 red chalk drawings of dissected bulbs of Guernsay lily that have no numbering or descriptions.

D406 In grey card folder labelled, presumably by the artist, '*fleurs des Lise de Gerse*', and by William Hunter, 'Drawings of the Guernsey Lily by J. D.'. 6 red chalk drawings of flowers and parts of flowers of the Guernsay lily, no descriptions. Same artist as the other red chalk drawings.

D407 In grey paper folder labelled '*figurarim explanatio* Guernsay Lilly'.
Several lists of figures of Guernsey lily in different stages of growth, some dated 1725. pp 7.

Letter to James Douglas from:
D407.7 Dan Deering, Picadilly.

Coffee

D408 'A history of the use of Coffee'
An extensive work on coffee, limited parts of which were published in *The Botanical Dissection of the Coffee Berry* which was published together with *A description of the Guernsay-Lilly,* London (1725), and in *Arbor Yemensis fructum Cofe ferens: or a description and history of the Coffee tree,* London (1727) and *A Supplement to the description of the Coffee Tree,* London (1727). Amanuensis, G. Douglas, with corrections by James Douglas. pp 268. [BT 19.2]

D409 Two slips that have become detached from D408.

D410 '*Index Auctorum*'
Not included in the list of contents, but obviously related to D408. pp 17. [BT 19.2]

D411 Part of drafts for 'The History of Coffee in Europe' and 'The Culture of the Coffee plant' which form part of 'A history of the use of Coffee', D408. Amanuensis, G. Douglas. pp 13.

D412 Notes on authors on Coffee.
Amanuensis, G. Douglas. pp 30.

D413 (?)Part of draft of paper 'The Botanical Dissection of the Coffee Berry', read to the Royal Society on 18 Mar. 1724/25 (JB) and subsequently published with the *Description of the Guernsay-Lilly* (1725), though it differs substantially from the published version. pp 18.

D414 Part of a draft for *A Supplement to the description of the Coffee Tree* (1727) but differing from the published text.
Amanuensis, G. Douglas. pp 4.

D415 Part of draft of paper 'On the Coffee plant in general' said to be read to the Royal Society, but no record in JB.
Amanuensis, G. Douglas. p 1.

D416 Records of observations on the coffee plant.
Amanuensis, G. Douglas, with additions by James Douglas. pp 3.

D417 Letter to James Douglas from B. de Jussieu, Paris, 20 Aug. 1728.

Coconut

"Dr Douglas showed the Society several coconuts in the different sections, transverse and lateral." (JB, 25 Jan. 1727/28).

D418 'A botanical Dissection of the fruit of the coco tree, J. D.'
Draft of papers read to the Royal Society, 8, 21, and 29 Feb. 1727/28.
Amanuensis, G. Douglas. pp 3. [BT 19.19]

"A letter from Mr Miller, gardener at the Physic Garden at Chelsea, dated 20 Feb. 1727 to Dr Douglas, was read concerning the vegetation of the coconut." (JB).

"A further part of Dr Douglas's description of the fruit of the coco tree was read." (JB 22 Feb. 1727).

"The conclusion of Dr Douglas's Botanical description of the coconut was read." (JB 29 Feb. 1727).

D419 '*Fructus Coco*'
Information about the coconut acquired on the Island of St Thome. Possibly from Robert Lightfoot, surgeon on a slave ship, who had spent some time on the Island, and was a friend of James Douglas (see letter D642) and who is referred to in D418.2.

Lilio Narcissus reginae

There is amongst the Douglas papers no material relating to this plant which Douglas described to the Royal Society 7 Mar. 1727/28 (CP x {ii} 6). The bulbs given to Thomas Fairchild three years before had just flowered on 1 Mar., the Queen's birthday, and the species was therefore named *Lilio Narcissus reginae* (*Hippiastrum reginae*).

The Tulip

D420 'The tulip as it appeared 6 May 1728'
Notes on the Tulip, including bibliography of writers on the tulip. Probably notes for an extensive planned work on the tulip of which only the historical section, an account of its classification and of its bulb, has survived in 'Of the Tulip'. MsH 539. Amanuensis, G. Douglas. pp 16 [BT Ac.2]

A letter to James Douglas from:
D420.1 From a grateful friend, part only.

D421 Folder labelled '*Tulipa*'.
Verso - 5 drawings of the tulip and containing 7 loose drawings of tulip bulbs.

Ipecacuanha

D422 'A short account of the different kinds of Ipecacuanha by J. D.', 17 Oct. 1728.
Amanuensis, G. Douglas. pp 7.
And 'A short account of the different kinds of Ipecacuanha'.
Amanuensis, G. Douglas. pp 12.

These are two drafts of a paper to the Royal Society, 14 Nov. 1728 (CP x {ii} 10) and subsequently published *Phil. Trans.* **xxxvi** (1729/30) 152-158.

D423 Notes for an extended work on Ipecacuanha by James Douglas.
Amanuensis, G. Douglas. pp 31.

Arum

D424a Notes on authors on the *Arum.*
Amanuensis, G. Douglas. pp 5.

D424b Records of observations on the *Arum*, Apr. 1728 - Feb. 1728/29.
Amanuensis, G. Douglas. pp 35.

D424c In a folder made from *A List of the Governors of the London Workhouse* and labelled 'The *Arum*', 10 Feb. 1729.
An account of the *Arum*
Amanuensis, G. Douglas. pp 43.

D424d An account of the *Arum*, very similar to D424c.
Amanuensis, G. Douglas. pp 33.

D424e Part of an account of the *Arum.*
Contains "whatever discoveries it shall be my good fortune to make ... I shall be always ready to communicate to this honourable Society." suggesting that this paper was read to the Royal Society, but there is no record in the JB that it was read.
Amanuensis, G. Douglas. pp 18.

Chocolate

D425 '*Index Auctorum qui de arboro Cacoa scripserunt*'
With brief descriptions of their works.
Amanuensis, G. Douglas. pp 20.
This belongs to 'The History of Chocolate', MsH 560, which contains a note by William Hunter "The History of Chocolate in order to be stitched; yet wanted the 3 indexes of Authors".

D425a Drawing of cocoa bean pod(?).

Tea

D426 *'Index Auctorum'*
with brief descriptions of their work.
Amanuensis, G. Douglas. pp 18.
This belongs to 'Of Tea', MsH 559, which lacks the bibliography that is listed in the Index of contents.

Logwood

D427 Notes on the Logwood tree, mainly in James Parsons's hand, with additions and corrections by James Douglas. pp. 25.

Letters to James Douglas from:
D427.20 Andrew Millar, ND.
D427.21 Will. Maitland, ND.

D428 Further notes on the Logwood tree, mainly in James Parsons's hand, with additions by James Douglas. pp. 49.

D429 'A description of the Logwood tree'
Amanuensis, James Parsons. pp. 25. [BT.19.7]

Contrayervia

D430 In a folder labelled *'Contrayervia'.*
Notes on the writers on *Contrayervia* in unidentified hand, with additions by James Douglas. pp. 22

Absinthium

D431 *'Absinthium'*
Common wormwood. Notes pp. 22.

Lichens

D432 *'Lichen Terrestris'*
Notes on lichens.
In a folder made from a proof plate for the 'Osteology', marked by James Douglas 'Le proof que Mr le Docteur a corrigé'. pp 6. [BT Ac 2]

D432.4 Verso - Printed advertisement for William Dale, retailer of hams and tongues.

D433 Notes on lichens.
Amanuensis, James Parsons. pp.14.

Letters to James Douglas from:
D433.12 Jno. Periam, ND.
D433.3 Jno. Blackstone, Fleet Street, ND.

D434 Fair copy, by James Parsons, of description of lichens. pp.11.

D435 5 red chalk drawings of lichens by James Parsons, with descriptions. pp.7.

Miscellaneous botany papers

D436 Alphabetical list of plants from *Lavendula augustifolia* to *Utica vulgaris.*
Amanuensis, G. Douglas. pp3.

D437 Alphabetical list of plants A-Z.
Left-hand column, Latin name; right-hand column, alternative name with initials of author.
Amanuensis, G. Douglas. pp.20.

D438 Alphabetical list of plants under various headings, e.g. *Herbe sponte nascentes, Herbae in Hortis Culturae,* etc.
Amanuensis, G. Douglas. pp.21.

D439 Classification of plants from Joseph Pitton Tournefort *Institutiones rei herbariae*, Paris (1700), with added descriptions of some plants by other authors.
Amanuensis, W. Tullideph. pp. 81.

D440 A classification of plants from John Ray's *Synopsis methodica* (1696).
Handwriting of Patrick Blair. pp. 6.

D441 Notes for 'An account of Mr Ray's life and writings'. MsH 593.
Amanuensis, G. Douglas, with additions by James Douglas. pp. 10.

D442 Transcription by James Douglas of the inscription on William Turner's tombstone in the south-east wall of St Olive's Church, Hart St, London. p. 1.

D443 List of botanical authors in chronological order from 1540-1727.
Amanuensis, G. Douglas. pp. 29.

Letters to James Douglas from:
D443.3 Eliz. Chitty, ND.
D443.4 Catherine Hyde (Duchess of Queensbury), 22 Oct. 1732.
D443.9 M. Horsley, ND.
D443.10 Jno. Beaumont, 10 May 1735.
D443.14 John(?) Gira, ND.
D443.16a John Douglas, sending Latin verse on conception by David Kinlock.
D443.1g Chas Morris, ND.
D443.15 (?)draft of a letter.

D444 List of eighteenth century botanical writers arranged chronologically, 1716-1734.
Amanuensis, James Parsons. pp 18.

D445 *'Index auctorum Chronologicus'* from AC [BC] 450 - AD 1727.
Amanuensis, G. Douglas. pp 3.

'Auctores qui de plantis scripserunt' MsH 564.
Arranged chronologically with indexes.
Amanuensis, W. Tullideph, with additions by James Douglas; loose section in G. Douglas's hand, with other additions by unidentified hand possibly that of MsH 635.

D446 'Alphabet of Barrelierus's Catalogue'
Presumably based on Jacob Barreliero, *Plantae per Gallium, Hispanium et Italiam,* Paris (1714).
Amanuensis, James Parsons. pp 6.

Letters to James Douglas from:
D446.2 William Schaw, ND.
D446.4 William Luttrell, 24 Mar. 1737.

D447 Letter to Patrick Blair from Thomas Knowlton, 12 Jan. 1727 [with letter from J H Harvey, 3 Mar. 1975, relating to place-names and plant names mentioned in the letter, and letter from D MacClintock, 16 Mar. 1975]. [BT 19.20]

D448 Miscellaneous botanical notes in various hands. pp. 15.

D449 11 drawings of unidentified plants.
In grey folder. [BT 8.5]

D450 Four sheets of pressed leaves and seed pod, from plant figured in D449.8. [BT 8.6]

D451 Xerox copies of letters between Patrick Blair and James Douglas, from the Bodleian Library, Oxford.
Transcriptions of related letters, including letters between Patrick Blair and John Martyn, from the Bankesian Manuscript Collection, Natural History Museum, Botany Library.

Labelled by William Hunter 'Of the Flowers and Seeds of Plants'. MsH 561.
Amanuensis, G. Douglas.

Labelled by William Hunter 'Of Plants'. MsH 562. Deals with nutrition, vegetation of the seed, formation of the seed, fruit, *Radix et Caulis,* Hawthorns, etc, together with 'Preternatural affections of plants', Johannes Daniel Major *De Planta Montrosa Gottorpiensi.*
Amanuensis, G. Douglas.

See also C. H. Brock, 'James Douglas (1675-1742), botanist', *J. Soc. Biblphy. Nat. Hist.* **ix** (1978) 137-145.

Zoology

Invertebrates

D452 Notes on molluscs from various authors.
Amanuensis, G. Douglas.

D453 'Explanation of the picture describing the manner of sowing, gathering, and drying the Grana or Cochineal done by an Indian in the Bishoprick of Oaxaca in the Kingdom of Mexico in America' Sent to James Douglas, possibly by W Houston, a good friend of Douglas. Picture missing.

"The President communicated a letter from Dr Houston, dated at Kingston in Jamaica 9 Dec. 1730, serving to accompany an account of the way of manufacturing the Cochineal in the Valley of Oaxaca in Mexico." (JB, 1 July 1731)

D454 An account of the Cochineal sent to the South Sea Company from Vera Cruz; including experiments - by (?)James Douglas - on the dying power of different kinds. pp 4

"The Anatomy of a Lobster was read and the subject shown by Dr Douglas." (JB, 28 May 1707).

"Dr Douglas communicated a paper containing an account of the Spanish Scorpion and at the same time laid three of the same insects before the Society for their inspection". (JB, 2 May 1728). (Transcription of Paper, RB 13.81).

"A paper concerning the poison of the Scorpion was communicated and read by Dr Douglas." (JB, 9 May 1728).

Vertebrates

Fish

D455 Notes on authors on fish. pp. 6.

D456a Comments on Steno's opinion that the skate had no oesophagus, etc. p. 1.

D456 Notes on the dissection of a thornback (skate), 26 Sept., 28 Sept., 18 Oct., 1706. pp.44. [BT.22.5]

D457 In a folder made from a catalogue of pictures to be auctioned and labelled 'Description of the Thornback at Gresham College', 5 Feb. 1706/7.

i. A description of the parts of generation of a male and female Thornback, 12 Feb. 1706/7.

"A paper by Dr Douglas was read of the Anatomy of a Thornback and the subject itself shown." (JB, 12 Feb. 1706/7)

ii. A description of the stomach, gut, liver, gall bladder, pancreas, spleen and kidney in a Thornback, 19 Feb. 1706/7.

"The descriptions of the stomach, guts, liver, gall bladder, pancreas, spleen and kidneys of a Thornback were read. Dr Douglas showed the parts. He was thanked and desired to proceed in the anatomy of this fish." (JB, 19 Feb. 1706/7)

iii. A description of the heart and gills of a Thornback, 5 Mar. 1706/7.

"Dr Douglas showed the structure of the heart and gills of a Thornback etc. There was read a description of these at the same time." (JB, 5 Mar. 1706/7)

iv. A description of the brain, eyes, noses, mouth, tongues and the oval holes in a Thornback, 12 Mar. 1706/7.

"Dr Douglas showed the brain, mouth etc of a Thornback. He was desired to proceed." (JB, 12 Mar. 1706/7).

v. A description of the cartilages of a Thornback, 19 Mar. 1706/7

"A description of the cartilages of a Thornback by Dr Douglas was read." (JB, 19 Mar. 1706/7).

vi. A description of the muscles and nerves in a Thornback, 26 Mar. 1706/7

"A Description of the muscles and nerves of a Thornback was read and demonstrated by Dr Douglas." (JB, 26 Mar. 1707). pp.39. [BT 22.5]

D458 Three drawings, two of the pectoral girdle and one of the egg case of a skate. [BT 22.8]

James Douglas had a large number of drawings of the anatomy of the skate, but these were removed by John Hunter and are now in the collection of John Hunter drawings at the Royal College of Surgeons of England.

D459 36 coloured slides of Douglas drawings of dissections of skate, the originals of which are at the Royal College of Surgeons of England. Artist not identified.

Letter to Sir Hans Sloane from James Douglas, ND. (BL Sloane Mss 4085. f26) asking for the loan of Willoughby [*De historia piscium* ... (1686)] to see what he says about the Thornback.

D460 Account of the Dory.
Amanuensis, G. Douglas. pp 3.

D461 Account of the Dory.
Amanuensis, G. Douglas.

"The President showed the Society a monstrous Double Flounder which being viewed by Dr Douglas undertook to examine it and give the Society an account of it." (JB, 2 Nov. 1727).

"Dr Douglas communicated the observations which he had made on the uncommon flat-fish which was presented to the Society by Mr Surgeon Amyand under the name of a double Flounder." (JB, 9 Nov. 1727).

Amphibia

D462 'Of the Water frog'
Also contains information about salamanders, serpents, and lizards. pp 23. [BY 15.3]
Probably a transcription of an article by Edward Browne, son of Sir Thomas Browne, for it contains the statement, "My father advanced and proved ye brain to be ane appendix of ye spinal marrow which men had unhappily forgot ..." which comes

from Sir Thomas Browne, *Enquiries into vulgar and Common Errors* (1646) Book IV, Chap 5, "And therefore the brain, especially the Spinal Marrow which is but the brain prolonged".

D463 Notes on frogs from various authors.
Same handwriting as D460 with additions by James Douglas. pp 31. [BT 15.2]

D464 Notes on various authors on frogs, one page dated 18 Dec. 1710.
In a folder made from an advertisement for *A Sale of Valuable Plate*. pp 57.

D465 In a folder labelled '*Rana Aquatica*'.
A fair copy of notes on various authors on the frog, arranged chronologically in numbered sections, Aristotle to Daniel Tauvry, 1700, plus three sections that do not fit into the sequence, possibly forming an appendix. pp 102.

"Dr Douglas showed the skeleton of a frog wherein the vertebrae of the backbone with the os sacrum were not continued but in lieu of the vertebrae were three bones which continued the spine to the os femoris. He showed also the lungs of a live frog opened and the systole and diastole of the heart, with some parts like gutts continued from the lungs to the arms of which he promised a more particular account" (JB, 13 Dec. 1710).

D466 Notes on the anatomy of the frog and its behaviour 2 Apr. 1711, 15 Feb. 1712, 18 Jun. and undated notes.
In a patterned folder. pp 22.

"Dr Douglas showed the Dissection of the Male and Female Frog with observable differences between them as besides those of the sexes. The Male has a hard Callus or Protuberance at the root of the Pollux of both fore feet wanting in the female the use to be inquired into. The Testes of the male were very large in the Female the uterus, being blown up was very large. It was observed that the

Tuba Fallopiana was seated at a Great Distance from the Ovary which lay very high so as the Doctor judged the Fimbrie of the Tube could by no means be applied to the ovary, so that he supposed the ovum must be let loose into the cavity of the abdomen. He showed the lungs tho' very large were not bladders in the Lower Belly as in the Fowl. That the skin or cutis was fastened or tacked to the muscles on[ly] in some places and not every where as in most animals. The Doctor was thanked and desired to draw up a paper of his observations which he promised." (JB, 5 Apr. 1711).

"Dr Douglas's was read treating of and explaining the muscles moving the *Os hyoides* [in the frog] These are six, the first analagous to the *stylohyoides* in man, the second to the *caracohyoides*, the third to the mylohyoides, the fourth proceeds from the inside of the sternum the fifth he names *Geniohyoides itericos* from the lower jawbone the 6th a smaller than the rest proceeding from one of the little bones in the forepart of the lower jaw and here he observes the peculiar curious mechanism of nature to supply the want of Ribbs in this Animal by drawing down the loose Bag under the jaw and so letting the Air into it through the nostrils which by closing them and the mouth is after forced into the lungs. Since the thorax cannot be otherwise raised as in other animals." (JB, 19 Apr. 1711).

Letter to James Douglas from:
D466.13 Rebeckah Avery.

D467 Notes on the anatomy of the frog in the form of statements of the opinions of various authors against Douglas's observations, some from dissections on 16 and 19 Feb. 1712. pp 10.

D468 An account of the anatomy of the frog with an account of a dissection, 22 Apr. 1712. pp 8.

D469 In a folder made from syllabus of Douglas's Anatomy Lectures and labelled '*formulae Camerin-*

[an]nae', containing:
'Of the curious structure and constitution of the genital parts in a female frog big with little ones'

'Of ye female frog'
A paper read to the Royal Society, 21 Feb. 1711, (JB). pp 2. [BT 13.4]
This paper is the text of James Douglas 'Of the curious structure and constitution of the genital parts in a female frog, full of eggs' in Richard Bradley, *A Philosophical Account of the Works of Nature,* London (1721).

D470 Original drawings of the reproductive system of the female frog and two copies of a plate incorporating the figures.
Unsigned but probably by F. Boitard. These were shown to the Royal Society, 19 Jun. 1712 (JB). pp 8. [BT T.3]

"Dr Douglas brought an explanation in writing of the several figures of all the changes which frogs undergo from the egg to their complete formation with several figures being seventeen in all." (JB, 10 July 1712).

These drawings were published as illustrations to James Douglas' papers in Bradley, *A Philosophical Account of the Works of Nature* where they form Plate X, A + B.

"10 July 1712. The Royal Society. Dr Douglas showed the gradual process in the formation of the tadpole or bultread, to a frog; the placenta of a calf, the veins filled with red wax and the arteries with green, very delicately performed ..." *The Diary of Ralph Thoresby.* London, 1830.

D471 'Of the genital part of a male frog and some particulars wherein it differs from the female'
pp 2. [BT 15.1]

"Dr Douglas's paper of the male frog read 28 Feb. 1711/12." (JB).

D472 In a folder labelled by William Hunter 'Drawings of the frog by J.D.'.
11 original drawings of the frog, some labelled F. Boitard, with three engravings made from them, probably by Boitard.

D472.9 Verso - Description of "a little case" supporting a broken limb when a patient has to be moved from his bed

D472.12 Verso - Notes on Mithridatis.

Reptiles

D473 Notes on the viper from various authors. pp 4.

Letters to James Douglas from:
D473.1 [John Kesson] asking for reference as to character. Bottom half of letter D475.8.
D473. 2 Matt. Lee, 16 Jan. 1736.

D474 Notes from various authors on the viper. Amanuensis, G. Douglas. pp 5.

D475 Notes of dissections of vipers. pp 18.

Letters to James Douglas from:
D475.5 R. Wyatt, 27 Apr. 1726.
D475.8 John Keeson, ND, bottom half of letter in D473.1.
D475.11 S. Wollaston, ND.
D475.12 Edward Murdoch, 4 Nov. 1736.

D476 In a folder made from *To the Right Honourable the Lords Spiritual and Temporal in Parliament assembled,* labelled 'Viper', and enclosed in a grey paper folder.

'The anatomy of the maxillar bones and teeth in a Viper with a description of the muscles that move them illustrated with figures drawn in the natural situation of the parts and distinct views of each bone and muscle separated'
The Ms also contains notes on the rattlesnake. Amanuensis, G. Douglas, and possibly another of

Douglas's sons, with extensive additions by James Douglas. Figures missing. pp 49. [BT 6.5]

Though these papers, where dated, relate to the years 1725-1736, James Douglas had long been interested in the viper.

"19 Jun. 1712. Then at a meeting of the Royal Society ... a letter from Mr Leuvenhock was read, and Dr Douglas's proposal for a more particular anatomy of the several animals; and he showed curious drafts of the dolphin and other he had been concerned in himself; and showed some vipers, snakes etc he had dissected, and some living ones, very beautiful." *Diary of Ralph Thoresby,* 1830 .

"Dr Douglas showed the foetus's of a viper, one in and the other cut out." (JB 26 Jun. 1712).

"3 July 1712. Royal Society where Dr Douglas showed a viper he had dissected with young ones distinctly to be seen in the several apartments uterus, and a very large one he had put in spirits of wine, the heart of which beat sensibly now, after twelve hours when he took it out." *Diary of Ralph Thoresby,* 1830.

"Dr Douglas in prosecution of his design of a comparative anatomy brought a snake and a viper in both which subjects all the parts were laid open to show the differences between the two species." (JB, 3 July 1712).

Letters to James Douglas from:
D476.1 P Gilkes, May 1726.
D476.48 John Green, ND.

D477 Coloured plate of a (?)rattlesnake, which had at sometime been used as a folder and labelled *'Figura Ranarum et Armandill:'.*

D478 Notes on authors on the turtle and tortoise. pp 33.

Letter to James Douglas from:
D478.33 Verso - Priscella Cooper, 15 Oct.

D478.10 Note to Mrs Hepden from James Douglas.

D479 Notes on authors on the turtle and tortoise. Same handwriting as MsH 612, with additions by James Douglas. pp 43. [BT 22.4]

D479a Notes on 'Du Verney's acct of ye tortoise etc' including notes on *Rana aquatica,* a carp (9 Dec. 1705), and '*Sur les plumes des oiseaux'.* pp 42.

A dispute developed between G. J. Duverney and Jean Mery in Paris *(Histoire de l'Académie des Sciences,* 1703, p 32) and Paul Bussiere in London over the structure of the tortoise heart. In Paris it was maintained that the ventricle of the tortoise heart was incompletely divided into three chambers; Bussiere (*Phil. Trans.* **xxvii,** 1710, 170) maintained it was a single chambered structure.

D480 Notes of dissection of a tortoise, 18 July 1712. pp 4.

"Dr Douglas brought a description of the parts of Generation of the Male Land Tortoise from Jamaica ... " (JB, 24 July 1712).

D481 In a folder labelled 'Some drawings of the tortoise'. 11 drawings of dissection of a tortoise, almost certainly by F. Boitard, and probably from the dissection of 18 July 1712.

D482 Drawings of the heart, blood vessels and lungs of tortoise, 5 Aug. 1715, with comment by James Douglas.
"The Shell of this tortoise which seems to be one of fresh water (because of a web between the foreclaws like a goose) was 10 inches long." [BT 16.7, T.7]

D483 'The anatomical description of the heart and blood vessels in the *Testudo marina* or Sea turtle' by J. D., 17 Oct. 1715.
Part read 27 Oct. 1715 (R.B.)
In this paper Douglas claims:

"I have always found two distinct cavities or ventricles separated from one another by a thick and strong muscular septum, or fleshy partition ... and communicating with one another by a large hole ... and in my opinion there's no reason for multiplying them with more."

With 2 figures - described D482.2. A third is mentioned D482(3) verso, but cannot be identified amongst the surviving drawings. pp 10. [BT 22.11]

D484 'The True Situs and Disposition of the vessels that arise from the basis of the heart in the *Testudo Marina* or sea tortoise with some account of its two cavities by J. D.', 9 May 1717.
This paper was read to the Royal Society on 9 May (JB).

D485 Notes on the dissection of a sea tortoise, 26 Aug. 1715 and 27 Aug. 1717.
With descriptions of drawings. These drawings have been numbered in pencil and those that fit the descriptions have been identified. Three sheets of drawings X, Y and Z probably also relate to the dissection as figures 2-4 have been cut out of them, though the other drawings cannot be identified from the descriptions. pp 8 and pp 5 of drawings. [BT 16.3]

D486 Four sheets of drawings which probably relate to the above dissections but are not described.

D487 Omitted.

D488 Description and rough drawing of the veins and arteries entering and leaving the tortoise heart.

D489 'The Anatomical description of the heart of a sea tortoise and all its blood vessels that are contained within the pericardium, explained in several figures drawn from life'
No list of figures given. pp 5. [BT 16.7]

"The anatomical description of heart and blood vessels in the *Testudo marina* or Sea Tortoise" [by James Douglas] (JB, 27 Oct. 1715).

D490 Fig 1 - shows all the viscera in the hollow of the shell taken out and rested on a table.
Fig 2 - shows the muscles on ye backside. 17 Sept.
The figures probably reused in D494.

D491 Notes on the muscles of a tortoise.
24 Sept. In paper folder. pp 4. [BT 22.4]

D492 Notes of a dissection of a tortoise in unidentified hand, with additions by James Douglas, with description of the figures. 26 Sept.
Letters have been given to the descriptions and three of the drawings identified. pp 12 and 3 figures. [BT 22-20]

D493 'An essay towards a new physiological and anatomical account of animals in the complete natural history of the *Testudo Marina* or Sea Turtle and the anatomy of its principal parts', viz.
The skeleton
The heart and blood vessels
The gullet and stomach.
With figures (no description of the figures). pp 41.

D494 A list of plates - presumably to accompany D493.

i. 'ye outside and inside'.
1 copy of plate, 2 figures cut from plate and original drawings for 3 of the figures.

ii. 'ye skeleton and bones of ye head'.
1 copy of plate and 5 original drawings for the plate.

iii. 'More of the bones with ye backside of ye muscles'.
No plate but 4 drawings possibly intended for plate.

iv. 'The foreside of ye muscles with particular ones'.
No plate, but 1 drawing corresponding to description.

v. 'The veins and heart in 4 views'.
Rough plan for plate and 2 drawings - 2 other drawings belong to D484.

vi. 'The heart and blood vessels opened'.
1 copy of plate and original drawing.

vii. 'The heart and blood vessels'.
2 copies of half the plate, 1 copy of other half, 1 copy of single figure from plate. 2 plans for plate and 5 original drawings.

viii. 'The stomach'.
1 original drawing.

The drawings are from different dissections by various unidentified artists.

"Dr Douglas showed the society some figures he had caused to be engraved for the natural history of the sea tortoise he was now printing." (JB, 5 Dec. 1717).

D495 28 drawings of the anatomy of the tortoise from different dissections by various unidentified artists.

D496 11 black and white chalk drawings on grey paper of the blood system of the tortoise.
Unsigned but probably by P. R. Fremont.

D497 Notes on the anatomy of the lizard from various authors. pp 7.

D497.2 4 lists of equipment in a chemical laboratory.

D498 2 drawings of a lizard, probably by F. Boitand.

D499 Drawing of a dissection of a lizard.
Such a drawing was shown to the Royal Society, 19 Jun. 1712. (JB).

Birds

D500 Notes on observations and dissections of birds.

D500.1	'*Volatilia*', general notes on birds.
D500.2	A pidgeon.
D500.7	Verso - '*Anatomia canis*', 17 Sept. 1704.
D500.8	'A swan's head', 7 Dec.
D500.13	'Dr Harvey *Gallina*', 30 Dec. 1704.
D500.16	'*Gallina foetani*', 19 Feb. 1705. pp 7.

D501 The ms[muscles] in a cock. 22 Oct. 1707. pp 16.

"Dr Douglas presented a paper to the Society giving an account of the anatomy of the Eyelids and *membrana nictitans* of an Eagle which was read. In this paper the Dr gives a particular description of the formation of these parts especially of the *membrana nictitans* where he gave a very exact account of an extraordinary contrivence of Nature in the muscles that move that part which is best understood by the paper itself." (JB, 27 Jan. 1714/1/5).

D502 In a folder labelled *'Phoenicopterus'*.
Notes on authors on the flamingo; notes on the anatomy of the bird and draft of a paper. pp 25.

"Dr Douglas showed the Society a preparation of a phoenicopter's tongue." (JB, 7 May 1716).

"Dr Douglas gave a paper on The Natural History and description of the *Pheonicopterus* or flamingo; with two views of the head, and three of the tongue, of that beautiful and uncommon bird." (JB, 24 May 1716).
Afterwards published in *Phil. Trans.* **xxix** (1716) 523-541.

He again showed the tongue of the flamingo to the Royal Society on 5 July 1739. (JB).

D503 Original drawings for 5 of the 6 figures that form Plate II in *Phil. Trans.* **xxix**, illustrating the above paper. Artist not known.

D504 2 black and white chalk drawings on grey paper of the tongue of the flamingo.
Probably by P. R. Fremont.

D505 In a folder made from p 698 of a newspaper sold by J. Head, and labelled 'The Anatomical history, description, use and figure of the bones, cartilages and muscles of the oesphag: trachea and tongue in the bird called *picus tricolor belloni* and the common green woodpecker in English'.
Notes on various species of woodpecker, 1 Feb. 1716/17-11 June 1717. pp 12. [BT 16.4, 22.3]

D506 In a folder labelled by William Hunter 'Drawings of the woodpecker by J D'.
3 sheets of fine drawings of woodpecker head, with descriptions.
Artist not identified. pp 11 [BT T.4]

D507 Drawing in ink of head of woodpeck.
Artist not identified.

D507a Original drawing and plate, engraved by M. Van der Gucht, illustrating 'A description of that curious Natural Machine the woodpeckers tongue etc' by Richard Waller, Esq., late secretary to the Royal Society. *Phil. Trans.* **xxix** (1716) 505.

"Dr Douglas showed the parts described by Mr Waller in the head of the woodpecker and took notice of some particulars wherein he thought Mr Waller had been mistaken." (JB, 18 Apr. 1717).

"The natural history of a very beautiful bird called *Garrulus Bohemicus* i.e. the Bohemina Jay or silk tayl by Dr Douglas was read." (JB 24 Jan. 1716/17.).

D508 'Description of a bird called Κοκκοθρυτηε in Greek and the haw finch or gros beak in English' by J.D. 13 Feb. 1717/18.
2 descriptions of the bird and 3 sheets of fine drawings.
Artist not identified but probably the same as in D506. pp 17. [BT 22.6, T.5]

"Dr Douglas communicated a paper which was read containing a very curious and accurate description of a small bird not commonly seen in England called Gros beak." (JB, 13 Feb. 1717/18).

"Dr Douglas explained the contrivance where by the parrot moves the upper bill and showed likewise the same motion to found in the Bills of the Swan, the Goose, and the Duck and thence supposed the same in most if not all kinds of Broad Billed Bird." (JB, 13 Nov. 1718).

D509 In a folder labelled 'An appendix or supplement to the Anatomy of the Bustard in a description of a large membranous bag situate in the neck of this large fowl by [JD]'.

Notes on a large bustard sent to James Douglas from Cambridgeshire, with a letter from H. Johnson, Whitehall, 13 Feb. 1741, transcribing a letter from his sister relating to obtaining a bustard for Douglas and how it should be killed. pp 18. [BT 11.5]

Letters to James Douglas from:

D509.2 M. Gower, Billhill, 28 Nov. 1736.

D509.3 J Anderson, Munmuth Court, Hedge Lane, London, ND.

D509.4 Ann Collins, ND.

D509.5 Cover to letter to the Revd Dr Thirlby at Jesus College, Cambridge from H. Gerigh.

D509.8 Bill to Mr le Docteur Douglas, 28 Mar. 1737, *Pour un mois. Pour papier et Plume,* 3:6.

Dr Douglas gave to the Royal Society a paper on the bustard (JB 28 Apr. 1737). (A transcription of the paper, RB.20.263.)

D510 Drawings of a (?)waxwing, artist not identified.

D511 i. 'Philosophical and Physical observations concerning the hatching of chickens in Egypt by the heat of ovens, by Jo Veslingus, Kt.'

ii. Order and progress of the formation of Chicken in Eggs, by Volcherns Coiter.

iii. A Digression concerning the Egg and the air of the Egg.

Unidentified handwriting. pp 13. [BT F.3]

"Dr Douglas showed several curious figures and also the parts themselves in the hen relating to the ovary and the generation and exclusion of the eggs." (JB, 28 Feb. 1716/17).

"Dr Douglas showed the eggs of a hen that had been sat upon in order to hatch each day of sitting." (JB, 28 Mar. 1716/17).

D512 Drawing of the reproductive system of the hen.

For further work on reproduction in the hen and development of the chick see DF 68-77 where it forms part of Douglas's projected work on human reproduction.

Mammals

D513 Letter to James Douglas from James Petiver, 3 Mar. 1716, sending him an armadillo from "Buen Ayres". [BT 22.2]

D514 Notes on authors on the armadillo.
pp 16. [BT 22.7]

D515 Observations and rough draft of paper on the armadillo.
pp 19. [BT 22.2]
(There is also a note on the armadillo in D455.12.)

D516 'The Description and Natural History of the Animal called Armadillo or ye Hog in armour from South America by J.D.'
4 sheets of drawings of Armadillo.

"A paper from Dr Douglas describing the Animal called Armadillo, one of which was recently brought alive from Buenos Ayres." (JB, 5 Apr. 1716).

"Dr Douglas produced some very curious Figures of the Armadillo and skeleton. He showed the Society a worm of about 4 feet long said to have been taken out of the leg of a person in Guinea." (JB, 21 Jun. 1716).

D517 Notes of dissections and injections of dogs, 23 May and other dates, with notes of dissections of pigeon's eye, 25 May, the arteries of a cat, 2 June, the head of a goose, 29 June 1704. pp 4. [BT 22.9]

D517.3 & D517.4 Notes on Mr Cowper's injection techniques.

D517a Notes on the ear in fish, birds and mammals.

D518 'The use of the word *recimus* [bent back, turned up] by various authors as applied to parts of animal anatomy'. pp 2.

D518a Notes on the authors who have described certain structures in various animals, viz. *Bos,* Camaelon, *Canis, Caniculus, Dama, Echinus, Elphas, Eques,* etc.
Amanuensis as in MsH 612. pp 29.

D519 Notes on authors on the stomach of sheep and cows. pp 3.

D520 Notes for a lecture(?) - on the stomach of ruminants.
Possibly for item 3 in the comparative anatomy part of James Douglas's anatomy course, see D1. pp 5. [BT 10.2]

D521 Notes on dissection of a cow's foetus, 12 July 1704, and 27 Jan. 1705, and a ewe's foetus, 1 July 1704.

D522 Drawing of a (?)dog foetus with deformed head.

D523 'An account of the distemper that has raged so long amongst milk cows about London.
Drawn up by Mr Becket in Hatton Garden, read to the Royal Society', 2 Dec. 1714 (JB). pp 3.

D524 'The dimensions of a dolphin'
Thursday 12 June 1712, with dissection notes. pp 3.

"12 June 1712 ... attended the Royal Society where I found Dr Douglas dissecting a dolphin, lately caught in the Thames." *Diary of Ralph Thorsby*,

D525 Letter to James Douglas or William Stuckley from Richard Bradley on copulation in elephants.

A female elephant had died in London and come into the possession of Sir Hans Sloane, who offered it to James Douglas to dissect. Douglas replied (BL Sloane Mss 4058 f. 254) that its "enormous bulk quite frightens me from meddling with its dissection". It was then dissected by William Stukeley in Sir Hans Sloane's garden. But Douglas, in the end, could not resist the temptation to dissect the reproductive system, a description of which he added to William Stukeley's *Of the spleen .. to which is added some anatomical Observations in the Dissection of an Elephant* (1723) London.

D525a List of papers in the *Phil. Trans.* relating to comparative anatomy. p 1.

D525b Notes on two letters to the Royal Society from Swammerdam, concerning animals that having lungs are yet found to be without the Arterious vein ... *Phil. Trans.* **viii**, (1673), 6040.

D525c List of animal names ending with a, us, er, o, um, as, e, es, is, ii, x.

The Rhinoceros

James Douglas became interested in the rhinoceros when in 1739 one brought from Bengal was exhibited in Eagle Street, near where he was living at that time in Red Lion Square. His assistant and anatomical draughtsman, James Douglas, made drawings of it for him, and on 21 June 1739 he read a paper on it to the Royal Society. In October 1739 Douglas went to Holland to look after the Princess of Orange during her pregnancy and took the opportunity to examine with Wandelaar, the stuffed rhinoceros in the *ambulacrum* of the Leiden Botanic Gardens and obtained from Wandelaar, drawings of various parts of the animal. These drawings together with the drawings made by James Parsons, and other prints and figures of the rhinoceros, doubtless assembled for his paper to the Royal Society, where he compared early representations of the animal with his accurate description of it, are in the Hunterian Library, Av 1.17. For account of this collection of rhinoceros figures, see L. C. Rookmaaker, 'Two collection of rhinoceros plates compiled by James Douglas and James Parsons in the eighteenth century', *J. Soc. Biblphy. Nat. Hist.* **ix** (1978) 17-38.

Grammars

English

For James Douglas's place in English grammar, see Ian Michael (1970) *English Grammatical Categories,* London (1970) and Börge Holmbert, *James Douglas as on English Promounciation c 1740,* London (1956).

D526 In a folder labelled 'A fair copy of the regular and irregular English verbs in four conjugations', Amanuensis, Juvenile copy book. pp 89. [BT 1.6]

D527 'English Grammar perfect as far as the syntax' This is very similar to the 'Parts of Speech' portion of MsH 587 which generally incorporates corrections and additions made in this manuscript Amanuensis, Juvenile copy book. pp 289. [BT 1.7]

The parts of English Speech MsH 585.
The alphabet.
On pronunciation.
Amanuensis, I.J. Douglas.

Untitled. MsH 587.
First part deals with pronunciation and is a continuation of the last part of MsH 585 followed by 'The Parts of Speech in the English language', a revision of the first part of MsH 585.
Amanuensis, I. J. Douglas.

'The Fourth Part of Grammar called Syntax'
Amanuensis, David Watson.

'On Pronounciation' MsH 586.
A revised work on pronunciation. This has been incorrectly bound up. It lacks the section on the consonants l, m and n which are contained in MsH 585. Also the chapters on accent and emphasis, which occur in MsH 585 almost certainly belong to this Ms.
Amanuensis, I. J. Douglas.

D528 In a cover labelled 'English Declensions and Conjugations'.
Inside under title pages in James Douglas's hand:

i.. 'The Declinible parts of speech in the English language. Declined in proper paradigms.' *Celabitur Auctor.*

ii. 'An Essay towards a New Grammar for the English tongue in which all declinable parts of speech are delineated in proper paradigms'. Amanuensis, Samuel Boyse, with additions by David Watson and James Douglas. pp 103. [BT 103]

D528.100 Letter to Douglas from S. Lowe, 7 July 1740, praising the paper and its author.

D528.102 "I have perused this laborious and learned accurate Treatise". pp 103. [BT 3.3]

D528a 'Triphthongs'
Verso - 'List of words including all the urs shorte except'
followed by list of words. p 1.

French

D529 In folder labelled 'French Grammar by I. J. Douglas Jr'.
Amanuensis, I.J. Douglas, with corrections and additions by James Douglas. pp 532. [BT 3.1]

D529 64 Bill to James Douglas.

D530 French pronouns and verbs, very similar to D529, but in a different hand.
Amanuensis, Juvenile copybook. pp 177.

D531 'The sound of the letters of the alphabet in French' Incomplete. Amanuensis, I.J.Douglas. pp 55.

D529-531 may have been exercises set by James Douglas for his children. The following three manuscripts suggest that Douglas was working on a French Grammar for the young.

D532 In a coloured folder 'A catalogue of the particles or little words called Articles digested into the order of the alphabet, fully explained and adapted to the capacity of a young beginner'. pp 5. [BT 1.4]

D532 2 Letter to James Douglas from George Garnier, ND.

D533 In folder labelled 'Formation of the Tenses'. pp 9.

D534 'The General and casual signs whereby the genders and cases of nouns are known from one another' pp 8. [BT 1.4]

D535 'Substantive pronouns' p 1.
'Regular nouns substantive in the nominative case plural number' pp 2.
List of words. p 1.
Part in I.J. Douglas's hand.

Greek

D536 In sections, some sewn together in newspapers dated 1740.

i. In a folder made from *The Englishman's Evening Post and Universal Advertiser* 29 Mar. 1740, labelled 'The alphabet, the pronunciation of the letters, punctuation in the genders and parts of speech'. pp. 31.

ii. In plain folder labelled 'Parodia'.
The quality of the last vowels and syllables.
pp 32-144.

iii. In folder made from *The London Evening Post,* 15 May 1739, labelled 'Declensions'.
pp 145-176.

iv. In folder made from *The Englishman's Evening Post,* 26-28 June 1740, labelled 'Declensions'. pp 177-201.

v. In folder made from *The Englishman's Evening Post,* 21-24 June 1740, labelled 'Contracted nouns of the Third Declension'. pp 202-228.

vi. In a folder labelled *'Accentus'.* pp 229-356.

vii. In folder labelled *'Dialecti'.* pp 233-415.

viii. In folder labelled 'Verbs'. pp 416-494.

ix. In a folder labelled 'Verbs'. pp 495-561.

x. 'Defective Verbs'. pp 562-697.

xi. 'Nouns, pronouns, adjectives, adverbs, numbers, and Patronymicks' pp 698-804.

Amanuensis, I. J. Douglas. [BT 21.1-21.5]

D536.230 Letter to James Douglas from Darwin (no initial), ND.

Latin

D537 Bound Ms titled by James Douglas '*Declinatio prima, secunda, quarta, qunita'*
Amanuensis, I .J. Douglas. pp. 93. [BT 4.6]

D538 Bound Ms titled by James Douglas '*Declinatio tertia*'.
Amanuensis, I. J. Douglas. pp 78. [BT 4.5]

D539 Bound Ms titled by James Douglas 'Redundant Declensions, compound Declensions, Pronouns, Adjectives, Participles'.

The section on Pronouns is detached.
Amanuensis, I. J. Douglas. pp 79. [BT 1.5]

'Latin Grammar and Verification' MsH 584
Amanuensis, I. J. Douglas.

'Latin Grammar - Verbs' MsH 632
Amanuensis, I. J. Douglas.

'Genders' MsH 544
Amanuensis, I. J. Douglas.

D540 In a folder made from *A list of subscribers, officers and committees of the Society of the Encouragement of learning,* labelled,
'First, second and third declensions'. pp 39.

'Cases', pp 40-131.

'Nomina Numinum Ethnicorum a Decorum',
pp 132-161.

'Adverbia Comparativa adverbia liter sumpta',
pp 162-191.

'Verborum constructio', pp 192-222.

'Participle governing a genitive case', pp 223-259.

'Varia', pp 260-271.

'The similar persons of all moods and tenses', pp 272-273

Folder separated from its contents labelled by James Douglas,
'Defect: obsolete etc. Declensions redund.', p 274.

'Of the pronouns', pp 275-286.

'The Indiclinables - Adverbs', pp 287-302.

'Adjectives of one Termination', pp 303-411.

Amanuensis, Juvenile copy book to adult, with additions by James Douglas.
See also,
Latin Grammar MsH 589
Latin Grammar, Nouns MsH 582

'Latin Grammar, Verbs' MsH 583
All in the same hand as D540.

D541 In a folder made from *The Daily Advertiser,* 4 Aug. 1734 and labelled.*'Prima Declinatio* (corr)'

'Prima Declinatio 8 Mar. 1728', pp 1-14.

'The nominative case of the singular', pp 15-28.

'Of the Feminine Gender', pp 29-44.

In a folder made from a sheet of newspaper and labelled,
'Prima Declination Greek corrected', pp 45-56.

'Prima Declination Mas. Gen', pp 57-67.

In brown paper folder labelled *'Secunda Declinatio',* pp 68-89.

'Genders'
"Of what genders are nouns of the second declension that end in er?" pp 90-91.

'ius'
"Of what gender are nouns that terminate in ius?" pp 92-94.

'us'
"Of what gender are nouns that terminate in us?" pp 95-109.

'Cases of nouns of the third declension', pp 110-172.

'Third Declension', pp 173-234.

'The termination of the oblique cases in the Greekish words', pp 235-267.

'The termination of the other oblique cases', pp 268-274.

Lists of word ending in vowels, pp 275-364.

Miscellaneous notes, pp 365-370.

In James Douglas's hand, with a few additions by Samuel Boyse, I. J. Douglas and an unidentified hand. [BT 1.3, 4.2]

D541.365 Letter to James Douglas from Rich. Fitzgerald, 17 Oct. 1733.

D542 In brown folder labelled *'Prima Declinatio'* with inner folder made from *Proposals for Printing by subscription in Two Volumes, Miscellanies in Verse and Prose, Vol I Horae Lyricae ... Vol II Miscellaneous thoughts in Prose and verse* by I. Watts D.D., London, 15 Nov. 1733, and labelled, *'Prima Declinatio* Greek'
Latin nouns.
James Douglas and I. J. Douglas. pp 45. [BT 4.4]

D543 Word lists.
'Verbs according to their conjugation'
'Nouns according to their declension', pp 18.

List of European and Asian languages by their Latin name.
Amanuensis, G. Douglas. p 1.

'Latin Grammar' MsH 580
Verbs and Nouns.
Mainly James Douglas's hand, with additions by David Watson.

D544 Exercises in Latin Grammar. pp 21.

D545 Latin names of Gods, places, animals, plants, etc.
Amanuensis, Juvenile copybook - adult hand plus G. Douglas. pp 84. [BT 1.2, 1.8]

D546 Latin names of plants, etc.
Amanuensis, Juvenile copybook. with additions by David Watson and unidentified hand. pp 66.

D547 Latin word list.
Amanuensis, Samuel Boyse. pp 19.

'Inclinabilia' MsH 553
Amanuensis, Samuel Boyse.

D548 'The reduction of general terms to particulars', p 1.

D549 On metres in verse. p 2.

D549.2 Letter to James Douglas from Edward Knipe, ND. pp 2.

D550 Translation of part of Terence's play *Andria*. Verso - Letter to James Douglas from C. Mettcaffe, ND.

D551 Notes on Latin grammarians and other writers. p 1.

Horace

James Douglas had a great interest in Horace. He collected all the editions of the works of Horace from 1476, of which he published a catalogue.

Catalogus Editiorum Quinti Horatii Flacci ab an 1476 ad an 1739 quae in Bibliotheca Jacob Douglas,. London (1739).

After his death the collection was bought by the Chevalier D'Eon and was sold by public auction with the Chevalier's other books in 1813.

D552 Portion of a dictionary to Horace. Amanuensis, I. J. Douglas. pp 8.

D553 'The general kinds of verse made use of by Horace in his odes and epodes'. In a folder made from *A catalogue of the Fellows, Honorary Fellows and Licentiates of the Royal College of Physicians*, London (1735). pp 18. [BT 3.4]

D554 List of Latin words with translations. pp 3.

D555 Translations of Latin words and phrases. Amanuensis, Samuel Boyse. pp 2.

D556 Comments on translators of Horace's odes. Mainly by James Douglas, part written by Samuel Boyse. pp 12.

D557 In a folder labelled *'Haec omnia debent consisori id est salustiano stylo describi ne me agnoscant*

invidi'.
Notae ad notala Dacierii Baxteri, Bentleii et Beverlandi in Horatium, (1707). pp 133. [BT 3.5]

D558 Part of a dictionary to Horace.
Amanuensis, Samuel Boyce. pp 10.

James Douglas made a translation of Horace's first ode, which was printed. The British Library has two printed copies of the work, bound up with the ode itself 'from the first printed edition of his works by Zarothus at Milan 1474'. There is also a copy in the Dyce collection, Victoria and Albert Museum.

D559 Proof of pages 33-36 of James Douglas's *The first ode of Horace copied from a Ms in my collection of the editions of his works.*
Other pages have been used as folders round Douglas's osteological plates, DF 13.

'Index in *Horatium'.* MsH 576.
Amanuensis, Juvenile copybook - adult hand and Samuel Boyse.

'Horace's account of his own life'. MsH 577.
Amanuensis, I. J. Douglas.
'A Biographical and Geographical Dictionary for the whole works of Horace'. MsH 573.
Title in David Watson's hand, text in I. J. Douglas's, additions and corrections by James Douglas.

'A Biographical and Geographical Dictionary for the whole works of Horace ... for the use of schools' by David Watson. MsH 577.
Title page in Watson's hand, text in Juvenile hand.

'*Index in Horatium*'
Alphabetical index to words in Horace, A-J. MsH 578.
Amanuensis, Samuel Boyse.

'Latin Dictionary' to Horace, A-E. MsH 631.
Amanuensis, I. J. Douglas.

'Memoirs of the life of Horace, Prince of the Roman Lyrics, collected from his own writings'. MsH 633.

Concordance for the works of Horace. MsH 634. In a number of different handwritings.

'Dr Bentley compared with the Vulgate Edition'. MsH 579.
Amanuensis, Juvenile copy book - adult hand.

David Watson, in 1741, published a translation of the works of Horace, dedicated to James Douglas 'one remarkable for justice of taste and a nice discernment', and acknowledges the access he had to Douglas's most curious, most valuable and most perfect in its kind ever made of the collections of Horace'

D560 Meaning of Arab medical terms.
Amanuensis not identified. pp 3.

Personal Papers

D561 '*Catalogus Librorii ad Jacob: Douglass pertinentis ut Ultrajecti*'
29 July 1698. A catalogue of books, mainly medical, possibly a catalogue of Douglas's Medical Library. pp 7. [BT 29.1]
There is a transcription identifying the books. MsH 597.

D562 *Badds Junii* 4th *Die Lunae* 1694.
Part of a common place book, with transcription. pp 3. [BT 30.1]

D563 "Good Melis(?) without scruple courting gain
Tried physic, dice baffoonry all in vain ...". p 1.

D564 "We should never dispond tho' we find not all our enquiries attended with discoveries ... ". p 1.

D565 "Let me have but a little hole in heaven ...". p 1.

D566 "Unhappy England still in fortie one
By Scotland art thou deemed to be undone ... ". p 1.

D567 "Thus reasoned the mob
They like not Sir Robert ...".

'On the tumultous appearence at Westmr against the Excise, 15 March 1733' p 1.

D568 "Come listen you Toryes and Jacobites now
Your plot Mr Poultney as plainly will show ...".
p 1.

D569 Miscellaneous papers. pp 4.

D570 "The case of the Surgeons of the Royal Navy relating to the hardships they ly under from the apothecarys and Surgeons Hall Humbly submitted for redress to the Honble the Principal Officers and commissioners of His Majesties Navy".
Unidentified handwriting. pp 2.

D571 *'De Anna Regina'*
Latin verse.
Unidentified hand. p 1.

D572 'Lines on the death of Queen Ann, who died the day that the Schism Bill was to take place'
Unidentified hand. p 1.

D573 *'Epithalamium In Nuptias Celeberrimi Illius Herois Principis Auriaci, cum Armantissima Serenissima & Venustissima Anna Principe Regia Constorte'*
Latin verses, signed J. A. (John Arbuthnot?). p 1.

D574 'The Earl of Oxford not appearing at St James'
Verses.
Unidentified handwriting. pp 2.

D575 *'Epitaphium. In Obitum Nobilisimi Principis Gulielmi Illustrissimi Devoniae Ducis Regii Concilie Praesidis etc.'*
Possibly same handwriting as D572. p 1.

D576 "Here lies the Body of the Revd Mr Ford ...".
and
"Ye rakes & the Kind loving Damsells attend ...".
Unidentified handwriting. pp 2.

D577 "Hail happy Bride for thou art timely blest".
Handwriting, G. Douglas. p 1.

D578 'Flora at Autumn'
Handwriting, Samuel Boyse. p 1.

D579 'Liberty or the vision'
A Poem inscribed to George Lyttleton Esq.
Handwriting, Samuel Boyse. pp 2.

D580 Amyand *'Medicus Circumforaneus'*
Latin verses.
Handwriting unidentified. p 1.

D581 *'Epigramma. In bellum exortum inter Britannos et Hispanos'*
Latin verse.
2 copies, with variations in the 4th line.
Same handwriting as D572. pp 2.

D582 *'Laurea Poetarum Corona'*
Latin verse.
Same handwriting as D572. p 1.

D583 *'Studiosi Spanheimio Oratori et Mares Poeta Suo'*
Latin verses, "fixt upon the Academy Gate at Leyden under the printed title of an Oration of Spanheim's *De Corruptis Studiis, anno 1694*".
Unidentified handwriting. p 1.

D584 'To Learned M-----d thus Hanmer Spoke,
Doctor! this empty Scroll's a joke ...".
Unidentified handwriting. p 1.

D585 "Tis his Highnesses birthday and may he have many ...".
Unidentified handwriting. p 1.

D586 Scrap of verse.
Unidentified handwriting. p 1.

D587 "An experiment of a way of preparing a Liquor that will sink into & colour ye whole Body of Marble causing a Picture drawn on ye Surface, to appear also in ye inmost Parts of the stone".

From *Phil. Trans.* **i** (1665) 125.
Unidentified handwriting. pp 2.

D588 Scrap of inventory of house contents.
Unidentified handwriting. p 1.

D589 *The Old Coachman A New Ballard* to which is added *Labour in Vain,* (1742) London.

D590 *His Majesties most Gracious Declaration for the Encouragement of His Ships of War and Privateers.* 9th Mar. 1718.

This had been used as a folder so that it is in two pieces with parts missing down each side and in middle.

D591 *Proposal for Printing the Martial Achievements of the Scots Nation* by Patrick Abercrombie MD, 1710.
2 copies.
This had been used as a folder and labelled by James Douglas '*Cancer uteri et dolores in Vagine*'.

D592 *By the Queen A Proclamation.* 18 Feb. 1709/10.
Prayers for success against the French.
Has been used as folder, and labelled '*Affectus cutanei*'.

D593 *A True and Deplorable Relation of one Mr Sambrook ... who shot himself ...* (1708).
Has been used as a folder.

D594 H. S..E. Henricus Grovius ... (1737).

D594a *Simplicum Medicamentorum ... ex Dioscoride & Matthioli.*
Had been used as a folder for figures. p 1.

Correspondence

Letters to James Douglas from patients

D595 From John Ke(?), 13 Oct. 1711.

D596 From Alexander Dundas and Will Eccles, 25 Nov. 1721, relating to Lord Charles Kerr.

With an additional account, unsigned, of Lord Charles's health. pp 2.

D597 From Mary Crisp, 14 Oct. 1726.

D598 From Jos Gardiner, 24 June 1728.

D599 From W. Chaney, 20 Nov. 1730. [B.T. 27.2r]

D600 From M.H. to her sister, 22 Apr. 1732.
With an account of the state of health of her poor little boy - "to be shown to the Doctors" - With a prescription on the back for Master Herle(?).
In James Douglas's hand.

D601 From Edward Fleming, 22 Nov. 1735.

D602 An account of Mrs Secker's case from John Middleton and Sal. Pye, Bath, 18 Aug. 1736.

D603 2 letters, 1 from Chas. Goodall, Knightsbridge, 2 Aug., and 1 from Sus. Goodall, 29 Sept. 1736.
Verso of D603(1), possibly a translation by James Douglas of some classical passage.

D604 From Matt. Carter, Dublin, 12 Oct. 1741. pp 2. [BT 27.2f]

D605 From Elizabeth Adames, ND. [BT 18.ii.3]

D606 From Henry Ames, ND.

D607 From Lord Burlington, Cheswick, ND.
Verso - Part of List of Authors.

D608 From G. Davies, ND.
Verso - list of works of unknown significance, possibly in handwriting of D572.
And a description by James Douglas of a rhinoceros tossing a bear, in an engraving by Hans Sibmacher from J Camerarius, *Symbolorum ...* (1595).

D609 Fragment from Mary Doby, ND.

D610 Information annent Sir Archibald Grant's second son, ND.

D611 From Sam. London, Old Jewry, ND.

D612 From Judith Matthew, Hampstead, ND.

D613 From T. Moore, ND.
Verso - anatomy notes by James Douglas on fresh and dry specimens of bones and muscles.

D614 'Charles our 2d boy; continues very low ... ' ND.

Drafts of letters to patients

D615 "Madam
If I can do you no service its not for want of a good and particular in [ ] of your case ... " [BT 18.ii.1]

D616 To a Gentlewomen in Newport Pannel asking her for information about her state of health. [BT 18.ii.1]

D617 "My Lord
I am very sorry to hear of the Duchess of Leeds Indisposition ... " [recommending Dr Combs] (See also BL Sloane Ms 4043 f. 60).
Verso - letter from John Wilmer, ND.

D618 "In the distinct acctt you gave me of this Ladys case in your first letter ... " pp 2.

D619 Fragment.
"... I have the choice of three excellent wet Nurses if my Lady is not provided"

D620 "If Miss should be taken with a sickness at Stomach or reaching to vomit and very hot ..."
Verso - letter to James Douglas from George Gordon. [BT 18.7]

General correspondence

D621 From James Hunter, 2 May 1711.
Verso - accounts Jan. to Apr. for medicines.

D622 2 letters from J. Woodward, 22 Jan. and 23 Jan. 1713.

D623 From Mary Collins, Woodlands 6 Jan. 1718, Servant to Lady Winchelsey.

D624 Captain Matthias treatment to me in the ship upon the Coast of Africa, Anno 1726. H Lightbody or R J Lightfoot.
Rough draft and fair copy, pp 6.

D625 From Alexander Monro *primus,* Edinburgh, 31 May 1731.

D626 2 letters from George Martine, St Andrews, 11 June 1733 and 4 Aug. 1735. pp 3.

D627 Correspondence between James Douglas and William Cowper.
Cowper accused Douglas of having claimed a discovery relating to the muscles of the neck and back which Cowper had described and published in *Phil. Trans.* **xxi** (1691) 132.
Draft of letter from Douglas to Cowper, asking for reference to Cowper's work, a reply from Cowper and draft of letter from Douglas to Cowper acknowledging Cowper's priority in the description.

D628 From Mat. Forhead, ND.
An account for work done for Madam Douglas and a letter to Dr Douglas requesting to be paid and regretting to hear of the death of Madam Douglas, James Douglas's first wife.

D629 Letter from his sister-in-law, Jane Douglas, wife of Walter Douglas, Sheerness, ND.

D630 Letter form Ar. Douglas about General Douglas's old servant, James MacQueen, 16 Oct. 1717.
Verso - list of authors of unknown significance.

D631 From Th. Kennaway, Shandoes St, ND.
(Kennaway may have been a cousin).
Verso - list of patients. [BT 2.4]

D632 Draft or copy of a letter from Jane Douglas, St Christopher, 28 Sept., to 'My Lord', with two or three corrections by James Douglas, interceding on behalf of her husband after his trial for maladministration in St Christopher.

Drafts of letter by James Douglas.

D633 "Sir
I payed you for ye Republic ..."

D634 Scrap of letter signed Ja. Douglas.

Transcriptions and miscellaneous papers

D635 Letter from Nat. Blackerby to his sister, Chappel Street, 21 Jun. 1723, in which he accuses Dr Beal of impersonating Dr Douglas.

D636 Scrap of letter to "Madam" from Shom. Prigge(?) Verso - notes by James Douglas.

D637 Reference to a Latin work.

D638 List of countries in Latin.
Th. Kennaway's handwriting, with a list of references to numbers of the *Phil. Trans.* containing articles of interest to James Douglas.

A list of cities by their Latin names. pp 2.

D639 Part of a bibliography, pp 5. [BT 27.3]

Much of James Douglas's correspondence survives because he used the backs of the letters on which to make notes.

D642 Transcription of letters which have been used for making notes, arranged alphabetically, with biographical details of correspondents and their location amongst his papers.

D643 Transcriptions of James Douglas's drafts of letters with their locations.

D644 Transcriptions of letters from James Douglas held by other institutions.

D645 Miscellaneous material relating to James Douglas.

D646 Miscellaneous material not directly connected with James Douglas.

D647 Drawing of *Scarabaeus impennis tardipes,* artist unknown.

Experiments on this beetle were described in a letter to Alexander Stuart from Henry Baker, *Phil. Trans.* **xl** (1740) 441, but this is not the drawing used to illustrate this paper.

D648 Drawing of male child.

D649 In velum folder labelled 'Matt Richmond 1719'.
'A Table of the principal matters contained in the Aphorisms'
[based on Daventer], James Houston. pp 31.

D650 Fragment of advertisement for 'A Pleasant Liquor'.

D651 Engravings relating to amputations by M. Verduin of Amsterdam presented to Monsieur (?) Burgomr. of Amsterdam and Ambassador to King William the 3rd.

DOUGLAS FIGURES

James Douglas planned an illustrated Osteology. He started work on it before 1713 and worked on it for the rest of his life.

The 'Old Osteologies'

DF1 Very small drawings of bones and plans for their arrangement in plates, together with some larger drawings, with a description (DF1.50) by James Douglas of two of the drawings.
Artists, A and possibly F. Boitard. 75 items. [BT D.8].

DF2 In a folder labelled by William Hunter 'Dirty Proof of the old small bones by J D'.
9 plates of engravings of bones, one of which is signed 'F Boitard *fecit*'. Together with original drawings for the engravings, 6 signed F. Boitard and dated 1713. 14 items.
This has been taken as the first 'Osteology', 1713.

DF3 In a folder labelled by William Hunter 'Drawings of bones chiefly the old figures of bones by J. D.'.

DF3.1 - 3 Three approximately similar schedules of figures, one dated 1717.

DF3.4 A slightly different schedule.

35 plates arranged according to schedule 1, some of the plates numbered by James Douglas, the others identified from the descriptions. Original drawings for the plates except plates 19, 22, 23, 29. Some of the drawings have been reused from the 1713 'Osteology'.
Artists, F. Boitard and others. Engravers, F. Boitard, M. van de Gucht, R. Smith.
This is taken as the second 'Osteology', 1717. [BT 10, 2a, E7]

"On 27 November 1718 Dr Douglas showed some very curious draughts of ye bones of ye human skeleton for a new Osteology." (JB).

DF4 Miscellaneous drawings and engravings resembling those in the 1713 and 1717. 'Osteologies' but which do not fit any of descriptions in the schedules. 40 items.
Artists, F. Boitard and others. Engraver, C. Dupuis.

DF5 In a folder labelled by William Hunter 'Dirty proof of the old Figures of muscular attachments by J. D.'.
18 engravings of muscular attachments, some signed F. Boitard, 1713.

In a folder labelled by William Hunter 'Drawings, chiefly the old figures of Ligaments and Muscular Attachments by J. D.'
Original drawings for all but 4 of the plates. 20 items.
Drawings for which there are no engravings. 14 items.
Artist, F. Boitard. Engraver, F. Boitard(?). [BT J.8]

The 'New Osteology'

Douglas expanded his plans for his Osteology and employed better artists and engravers

DF6.1 An incomplete draft of an advertisement for his 'Osteology'. In this he mentions the gift of £500 from George I to help towards its publication. This advertisement appears at the end of Douglas's *Description of the Guernsay-Lilly* 1725.

"This is to give notice, that the whole work being nearly completed, he intends in a very little time, to publish on a large imperial paper, the first part of his *Osteographia Vetus ac Nova,* containing all the bones in an adult Human Body, drawn and engraven by the best Masters in a great variety of instructive views, and all as large as the life; with a short description explaining each figure. The rest of this great work will follow as speedily as the business of his profession will allow."

DF6.2 Another incomplete draft of the advertisement, differing from the first.

DF6.3 Incomplete draft of an introduction to 'Osteology'. Amanuensis, G. Douglas.

DF6.4 A draft schedule of plates.

Douglas presented to the Royal Society an account of his proposed *'Osteologia Universalis Pars Primus'* with a brief description of the thirty plates of which it was to be composed and of the other components of the whole work, viz. The History of Osteology from Hippocrates down to the Arabians. The weight and dimensions of every bone in one skeleton with the chemical analysis of the whole. To which is added a short explanation and etymology of all the terms used by the Greek writers on this part of anatomy" (C.P. XII.ii.29, 24 March 1725/26).

"Dr Douglas showed the Society 43 proof plates of his book of Osteology, now printing, containing the different views of the several bones of the human skeleton." (J.B., 20 June 1728).

DF7.1 Schedule of 30 plates for Part 1 of the 'Osteology'. In James Parsons's hand, (therefore post 1736) slightly different from the Royal Society schedule.

DF7.2 A set of plates that corresponds with the schedule.

DF7.3 Original drawings for the Plates except Plates 3, 7, 16, 17, 20, 25 26, 29. One set of drawings is in a wrapper made from a letter addressed to M. Claude Dubosc, from Thomas Minest.

Artist C, together with one or two figures from earlier 'Osteologies'. Engraver not known but possibly Claude Dubosc.

DF8 Missing.

DF9.1 A schedule of 30 plates for the second part of the 'New Osteology'.
In James Parsons's writing.

DF9.2 *'Ossa Conjuncta'.*
A detailed description of the first 26 plates for the second part of the 'Osteology', in James Parson's writing, [BT J.9]

DF10 28 engraved plates for the second part of the 'Osteology'.
Possibly plates XXVII and XXX would have come from the 1717 'Osteology'. There do not exist loose fine copies of all the plates. Some time in the 19th century a number of the 'Osteology' plates were bound up and now form Ay 2.20 in the Hunterian Library. The volume contains the only fine copies of some of the plates.

DF11 Original drawings for the second part of the 'Osteology', except Plates III and XV.
Artists, F. Boitard, B, C, and James Parsons.
Engravers, M. van der Gucht, possibly Claude Dubosc and others.

There are also bound manuscripts covering other components of the proposed work.

'Introduction to Osteology' MsH 544.
'History of Osteological figures' MsH 566.
These two manuscripts represent the final form of earlier attempts to cover the history of osteology, i.e. MsH 546, MsH 548 and MsH 567.

'The Greek terms of osteology' MsH 588.
'Descriptions of the bones with their dimensions' MsH 589.
'Description of the human sceleton from the Bones of the Pelvis inclusive downward' MsH 590.

In a folder labelled by William Hunter, 'Corrected and lettered proofs of the Osteology'.
A set of plates for Part 1 of the 'Osteology' (plate IV missing) together with proofs of most of the plates with corrections, lettering and numbers added in red chalk and with attached descriptions in writing of James Parsons with corrections by James Douglas. Plates XI-XXVII with new

descriptions and suggested corrections by William Hunter.

DF12 Plates I-VI.

DF13 Plates VIII-XIII.
In folder made from proof pages of Douglas's '*First Ode of Horace*.

DF14 Plates XIV-XX.

DF15 Plates XXI-XXVI.

DF16 Plates XXVII-XXXII.

DF17 List of Osteology figures differing from that of the 'Osteology'.

Douglas's 'Osteology' was never published. William Hunter hoped to publish it postumously.

"We have four large folio books of figures of bones, viz. Cheselden's, Abinus's, Sue's and Trew's, besides one which was long expected from my old Master and friend, Dr James Douglas, and which I wish very much to have time to publish, as the plates are all in my possession." William Hunter *Two Introductory Lectures* (1784).

Possibly the added corrections and descriptions by William Hunter relate to this proposed publication.

While the 'Osteology' was never published, one set of plates was given to Bernard Seigfried Albinus, either by James Douglas, who was acquainted with him, or by William Hunter, who visited him in Holland in 1748. This set was sold at the Sale of Albinus's Library in 1771 and may be the set which is now in the Library of the University of Leiden.

DF18 In a folder labelled by William Hunter 'Drawings of Bones chiefly of the 'New Osteology'.
2 plates with original drawings that are not described in the schedule of plates for the 'New Osteology'.
The original drawing for a plate in Ay. 2.20 which does not form part of the 'Osteology'.
Artist and Engraver not known.

DF19 23 drawings of bones not used in the 'Osteology', Artist, C.

DF20 24 black and white chalk drawings of bones on grey paper.
Some signed P. F. Fremont and dated 1718 and 1719. Some are very similar to figures in Part 1 of the new 'Osteology', but not identical.

DF21 3 drawings of the scapula labelled Du Flos.
2 drawings of the scapula labelled Henriel.

DF22 In a folder labelled *'Osi nasi'*.
9 red chalk drawings of bones of the nose region. These could be illustrations for Douglas's 'Of the nasal bones', MsH 545, the scheme for which included *'figurae'* but gives no description of the figures.
Artist, C.

DF23 A notebook containing descriptions of drawings of the ear and related structures.
13 drawings, in pencil and ink and wash, of the ear. Artists, B and others.
One plate of the ear from Heister, *L'Anatomie*, Paris (1724).
At the back of the notebook are descriptions of:
'Anchylosis - Mr Simons'. Descriptions of figures of an anchylosis of the elbow joint.
'Maxil. J. D.'
Description of "a j. which the aveoli are for the most part closed up and the bone itself narrower than ordinary - for Mr Amiens".
A list of figures of cranial sutures.

DF24 In a folder labelled by James Douglas, *'Suturae Captis'*.
4 pencil and wash drawings of sutures of the skull.
Artist, B(?).

DF25 One drawing of blood vessels on head of a bone.
Artist, B(?).

DF26 One drawing of teeth in jaw.
Artist, B(?).

DF27 In a folder labelled in pencil (modern labelling), 'Inferior extremity'.
2 red chalk drawings of the skeleton of the foot.
2 pencil drawings of the muscles of the foot.
Artists, B and C.

DF28 In a folder made from a drawing labelled by William Hunter, 'Drawings of the ligaments of the Thigh-Joint by J.D.'
A description of 3 figures headed *'Ligamentum femoris cum acetabalo'.*
3 figures in pencil and wash, that have tentatively been identified with the description.
2 other hip joint drawings, one in pencil, the other in pen and wash.
Artists, F. Boitard and B.

DF29 3 rough red chalk drawings of the shoulder-joint.
Artist, C.

DF30 Sketch and finished drawing of the head dissected to show articulation of the lower jaw.
Artist, C.

DF31 Miscellaneous skeletal drawings.

i. Sketch and finished drawing of the skeleton of the arm in two positions.
On the sketch is a note in French which does not refer to the drawings. Artist, F. Boitard.

ii. 14 drawings of skeletons by F. Boitard, two of which were used in W. Cheselden's *Anatomy of the Humane Body*, (1713), and one similar drawing by N. Bundock, and an ink drawing in different style with comments written in French.

DF32 i. Folder labelled *'Hemispherium Cranii Decr 27'.*

ii. Folder used by C Dubosc(?) to contain osteological drawings.

DF33 In a folder labelled by William Hunter, 'Figure of the Patella & Knee-joint by J.D. and of the

Diaphragme'.
A cover labelled '*Patella parisiis*' by James Douglas.
4 lists in James Douglas's handwriting of figures of normal and injured patellae.
2 engraved plates of figures of the patella.
Plate I is described at the end of James Douglas's bound manuscript 'On the patella', MsH 596; Plate II relates to the Table of Dimensions of the Patella in the same manuscript.

13 single engravings of the patella, 11 cut from the plates and 2 corrected engravings of a fractured patella which do not occur in the plates.
8 drawings of patellae including original drawings for the plates.
Artist and engraver, not identified. [BT E. 10]

DF34 Under cover labelled by William Hunter 'Drawings of the knee-joint by J.D'.
24 engravings of the normal and damaged knee-joint.
Lettered in pencil A-Z, P & Q missing.
Engraver, not identified. [BT. B5, E.10, E.14, K2].

DF35 Original drawings for plates A-F, & T-Z.
Artists: A-F Artist C, T Artist B, U-Z, Artist unidentified, black chalk or pencil drawings.

In the *Advertisement* at the end of James Douglas's *Description of the Guernsay-Lilly*, (1725), there is stated:

"The method in which the whole history of the Bones is to be Prosecuted, will be fully understood by that which is observed in the following Treatise now in Press, viz.

Osteographiae
Veteris & novae
SPECIMEN
or an
Essay toward a new Description
of the

Human Bones
Cartilages Origin and Insertion
Ligaments of all the Muscles
Together with the
Glandulae and *Sacculi Mucosi*
That belong to the
Tendons, Ligaments and Joynts
Contained in the
Description and Anatomical History
of the
PATELLA
or
Moveable Bone of the KNEE
Considered in a natural and diseased state
with Figures on Fifteen Folio Copper Plates

These engravings, DF33 and 34 together with the bound manuscript 'The Anatomy of the Patella ... with figures after the life, by J. D.' (MsH 568), are probably materials for this publication, though the Ms does not contain any description of the figures. In spite of being described as "in the press" it was never published.

At the Sale of Robert Nesbit's Collections (1761), there were sold to "Hunter", presumably William Hunter, "21 Finished Folio Copper plates (never published) to an intended 'Anatomical history of the Patella or Moveable Bone of the Knee' by the late James Douglas". The plates were engraved by Gerard van der Gucht. Presumably, these were the copper plates for these engravings. They have now been lost. Robert Nesbit was a pupil of James Douglas and married to the sister of Douglas's second wife, Martha Wilkes.

DF36 6 pencil drawings of the knee joint.
Artists, various.

DF37 17 black chalk drawings of the knee-joint.
Artist, same as DF35, U-Z.

DF38 2 pen and wash drawings of the knee joint and 3 pencil and ink outline sketches.
Artist, B.

DF39 13 red chalk drawings of the knee joint.
Artist, C. [BT 8.8]

DF40 1 red chalk drawing of a dissection of the knee to show a transverse fracture of the patella.
Artist, James Parsons.

Diseased Bones

Though in the description of the 'Osteology' that James Douglas gave to the Royal Society no mention was made of diseased bones, in the introduction to a bound manuscript on the subject, 'Diseases of Bones', MsH 547, Douglas says:

"In the course of my lectures at the Surgeons' Hall some years ago [1715-1717] I exhibited a very ample collection of morbid bones ... I am preparing figures of all the various instances of diseased bones in my possession ... These figures together with the explanation of them make them a considerable part of an Universal Osteology about which I have been now for many years employed ..."

The following collection of drawings of morbid bones is presumably part of this project.

DF41 In a folder labelled by William Hunter *'Exostoses'*

i. 3 drawings and a description of them by James Douglas, dated 2 July 1715. [BT D.84]

ii *'exostosis f. dolore'*
"Mr Rolfe lent me this bone ..."
6 drawings, including one which may be of the same bone as that illustrated in W. Cheselden's *Osteographia*, (1733) plate LI, fig 2.
Artist, B.

DF42 In a folder labelled by William Hunter, *'Exfoliationes & Separationes sez ossium'*.
15 Pencil and wash drawings, including one possibly from the same skull as that illustrated in Cheselden's *Osteographia*, plate XLII, fig 1.
Artist, B. [BT. D8e]

DF43 In a folder labelled by William Hunter, *'Magnitudae aucta et Diminutae'.*
9 pencil and wash drawings.
Artist, B. [BT D8.9]

DF44 In a folder labelled by William Hunter, *'Fracturae & Luxationes'.*
25 pencil and wash drawings, including one possibly of the same bone as that illustrated in Cheselden's *Osteographia*, plate XLV, fig 1.
Artist, B.

DF45 In a folder labelled by William Hunter, *'Caries Ossium'.*
22 pencil and wash drawings.
Artist, B. [BT. D8.b]

DF46 In a folder labelled by William Hunter, *'Anchylosis'.*
19 pencil and wash drawings, including one which fits a description by James Douglas *"Anchylosis tarsi et* that belonged to the Royal Society," possibly the same preparation that is illustrated in Cheselden's *Osteographia*, plate LIV, fig 3. And 3 drawings that fit the description at the back of the notebook in DF23, '*Anchylosis* Mr Simons'.
Artist, B. [BT D8.d]

DF47 In a folder labelled by William Hunter, *'Spina ventosa'.*
5 drawings in pencil and wash of deformed vertebral columns.
Artist, B.

DF48 In a folder labelled by William Hunter, *'Morborum ossium Figurae* by J.D.'
2 drawings in black and white chalk on blue paper; not by Fremont. 1 drawing in black and white chalk on grey paper; by Fremont. 3 drawings of deformed bones - pencil and wash; Artist B. One drawing in pencil fitting a description by James Douglas, "shews the bed in which the sword lay".
Artist B.

One scrap of paper with descriptions by James Douglas.

"A large foul ulcer.. in a man of 40... the bone that seemed to exfoliate." [BT D8.a]

DF49 4 red chalk drawings of fractured bones joined by callus.
One possibly of the same bone as that illustrated in Cheselden's *Osteographia*, plate LIV, fig. 2.
Artist, C.

DF50 In a folder made from a plate of the knee joint and labelled by James Douglas. '13 March 1728. Two anchyloses of the Knee'.
3 red chalk drawings numbered 1, 2 & 3, with a description of them by James Douglas.
Artist, C. [BT E.10]

DF51 One drawing in red chalk of an exostosed bone.
Artist, C.

DF52 3 sketches and 2 finished drawings of the "little French woman's" body and skeleton, by James Parsons. 28 Feb. 1739.

"[The little French woman's] body was shewn to the society. The person who delivered the account promised to procure an account of the case". (JB).

"Dr Douglas shewed a Draught of the skeleton of the little woman lately shewn to this Society and promised to produce the skeleton itself at some other opportunity for which he had thanks." (JB, 13 March 1739)
See also British Library. Add MS 4435 ff 247-249 b. 'The dimensions of the little French woman'.

In the Trustees 'Catalogue of the Hunterian Anatomical Collection'. (MR 20), p 402.
"Rickets
Two skeletons rickety one of a child another in a woman of forty a french woman whose height was diminished incredibly by the curvature of the bones."

> This entry also occurs in the *Catalogue of Anatomical Preparations in the Hunterian Museum* (1840), but is not recorded in Teacher (1900).

Besides the diseased bones figured for Douglas, which may also be figured in W. Cheselden's *Osteographia*, Teacher identified in the Hunterian Anatomical Collection four diseased bones that had been illustrated in Cheselden's *Osteographia*. James Douglas and William Cheselden were friends. In the Preface to *The anatomy of the Humane Body*, (1713), Cheselden acknowledges with great pleasure his "obligations to Dr Douglas that most Accurate and Indefatigable Anatomist, whose Assistance has been very useful to me in the compiling of this work, and who has oblig'd the World with an exacter Description of the Muscles, than any extant". References are made to Douglas's work in the text, and Plates I, II and III are taken from skeletal drawings made for Douglas by F. Boitard. In later editions the figures are replaced by the drawings Cheselden had made for his *Osteographia*.

Since it is know that Douglas had a large collection of diseased bones, and that Douglas and Cheselden were on such friendly terms, it is reasonable to assume that Cheselden used Douglas's collection for material to illustrate the section on diseased bones in his *Osteographia*, and that the bones in the Hunterian Collection that are illustrated by Cheselden also come from this source, rather than having been acquired by William Hunter from Cheselden, as has been suggested by Teacher.

The Female Reproductive System

The £500 given by George I to James Douglas was also to assist in the publication of a work "on the Diseases incident to women which depend on the vitiated structure of the parts". Though Douglas had collected material for this work it remained largely unorganised, though he did produce a scheme for the work.

DF53 A plan for this work, in James Douglas's handwriting, "*Gyneciorum prodromus* or an

introduction to the knowledge and cure of the diseases incident to women and the improvement of ye practice of midwifery".
The 8 parts in this schedule are listed below with the figures relating to each item.

DF54

Part 1 'A vertical section of the uterus with the adjacent parts in a virgin'
A sketch in pencil and wash and a finished drawing in black and white chalk on grey paper of a vertical section through the reproductive system and related structures in a non-pregnant woman.
Artist, P. R. Fremont(?).

Part 2 'The anatomy of the uterus in a woman with child and in child bed'.

i. Schedules of figures and two fuller descriptions of figures, none identical, relating to this and subsequent sections of the scheme.

ii A schedule of 27 *tabulae* of figures. 2 figures in pencil and wash, numbered 2 and 3, by Douglas, correspond to *tabulae* 2 and 3 in the schedule.

DF56 *'Index Tabulae'*
Descriptions of *Tabulae* 1-14 (*Tab.* 11 occurring twice with different subject matter). The last *Tab.* is not numbered but has been taken as *Tab.* 15.

Black and white chalk drawings on grey paper, numbered by James Douglas, that fit the numbered descriptions 1, 3 (2 sketches and a finished drawing), 4, 5, 7, and 1 black chalk on white paper numbered 9.

1 black and white chalk drawing on grey paper, unnumbered, that could correspond with description 12.
Artist, P. R. Fremont.

DF57 Descriptions of numbered figures, out of sequence, some of which can be identified under similar or different numbers in other schedules.

1 black and white chalk drawing on grey paper that fits *Tab.* 8a of schedule.

1 black chalk drawing on white paper that fits *Tab.* 8b of schedule.
Artist, P. R. Fremont.

DF58 Drawings that cannot be fitted into any of the above schedules.
1 series of 10 drawings in black chalk on white paper.
1 drawing of the uterus in black and white chalk on grey paper, numbered 7.
Artist, P. R. Fremont(?).

Part 3 'The situations natural and preternatural of the child in the uterus'.

DF59 3 incomplete pencil sketches of a foetus *in utero.*
2 black and white chalk drawings on grey paper and an engraving of a full term foetus *in utero.*
Artist, P R Fremont.

One incomplete pencil and wash drawing of a large foetus with umbilical cord round body.
Artist, B.

One black and white chalk drawing on grey paper of small foetus *in utero.*
Artist, P. R. Fremont.

One pencil and wash drawing of minute foetus *in utero.*
Artist, B.

Part 4 'An account of an hermaphrodite that was lately exposed in London'.

DF60 In a folder labelled by William Hunter.'Drawings of the *Pudendum Muliebre* with an Account of a Hermaphrodite' by J.D.

i. 'Some account of a young woman said to be an hermaphrodite, to be seen every day at Charing Cross, with the description and figure of the external appearance of the parts that serve for generation' 16 Feb. 1714/15.
In James Douglas's handwriting.

ii. The explanation of the figures.

iii. Three sheets of drawings in pen and wash.
Artist, B. [BT E8, K2, 5.5]

James Douglas read this paper to the Royal Society 17 Feb. 1714/15 (JB).

In James Parsons, *A Mechanical and Critical enquiry into the nature of hermaphrodites*, London (1741), two of Douglas's figures are reproduced with Douglas's description of them. These figures also occur in W Cheselden's *Anatomy of the humane body,* 2nd edition (1722), 4th edition (1732), and 5th edition (1740).

Part 5 'A delineation of the principle uterine *procidenses* and *exeversiones* with their explanations'

DF61 In a folder labelled by William Hunter.
'Drawings of *Procidentiae* by J. D.'

'Explanation of Figures'.
Description of figures 1-6: Three figures numbered 1, 2 and 6 by James Douglas, and a sketch for figure 2 that fit the description so numbered, plus one figure not described.
Artist, B(?). [BT E 8, 9]

DF62 Dissection notes that may refer to the case from which the figures in DF61 were made.

DF63 3 lists of figures that do not relate to any surviving drawings. 25 Sept. 1716.

DF64 25 drawings and engravings made from some of them.

DF65 2 unfinished pen and wash drawings which may be *procidentiae.*
Artist, B.

At one time James Douglas contemplated publishing a separate work on hernias and *procidentiae*. At the end of John Douglas's *Lithotomia Douglassiana*, (1723), there is the following advertisement:

"There will be published in a short Time a Treatise entitled *Hernias in Men and Procidentias in Women, anatomically explained. The parts fallen down in both Sexes being exactly delineated to the life* ... by James Douglas."

And in a letter to James Douglas from John Shipton, 5 March 1725, bound at the end of MsH 568, Shipton says "the hopes you have given us of seeing a piece concerning hernias from your hand ...".

Other material relating to hernias is in DF126.

Part 6 'The figures of some abortions and monstrous births observed in practice'.

DF66 In a folder labelled by James Douglas.
'Abortus' to which William Hunter has added, 'Drawings of'.
Drawings and description of an abortus, 10 Oct. 1710 .
Drawings and description of an abortus, 5 Mar. 1717.
Drawings and description of an abortus, 8 Nov. 1723.
Artist, B(?).

DF67 2 drawings of monstrous foetuses, 1 drawing of a duplicated vertebral column and deformed pelvic girdle, 1 engraving of a monstrous skull, etc.
Artists, B & unknown.

Part 7 *'Harverius redivivius* or the famous Dr Harvey's history of the formation of the chicken in the egg illustrated with figures and augmented with new observations'.

DF68 *'Inspectio ovarium'*
22 May 1716(?). Observations by James Douglas on incubated hens' eggs and 5 pen and wash drawings that fit the descriptions of figures made

at different stages of incubation, and 4 slips with separate descriptions.

DF69 *'Incubatio'*
27 Feb. 1717. Observations on incubated hen's eggs and descriptions of figures made at different stages of incubation and 8 drawings numbered by James Douglas that fit the descriptions, together with a list of the days on which the inspections were made.
Artist, D(?).

DF70 2 engraved plates containing figures from DF68 and DF69.
Engraver, unknown.

DF71 'The explanation of some figures in which are represented the whole series and progress of the gradual formation and growth of the chick in the egg from the end of the first day of incubation to the last day of the hens sitting when the chickens were hatched or came forth out of the egg by J.D'.

These descriptions are derived from those in DF68 and DF69 with additional descriptions and two additional figures.

DF72 2 engraved plates similar to DF70 that have been renumbered in pencil to correspond with the descriptions in DF71.

DF73 '1721 *Incubatio'*
Observations by James Douglas on incubated eggs - incomplete. [BT F4]

DF74 'The explanation of some figures, in which the yolks in the ovarium or vitellarii, the eggs perfectly formed in the uterus and the gradual advances made, during the whole time of incubation in the slow formation of the chick in the egg are fairly delineated after the life, by J.D.'

This Ms covers only a description of the egg. There are also:-

DF75 A list of figures of the reproductive system of the hen.

DF76 Another list, differing from DF75, of figures of the reproductive system of the hen.

DF77 3 engraved plates of the reproductive system of the hen and the structure of an unfertilized egg, with 7 of the original drawings. The figures in the plates have been numbered by the cataloguer according to the descriptions in DF75 and DF76.
Artist, D(?). Engraver, unknown.

Part 8 'A catalogue of authors that treat of women's diseases and give the anatomy of the parts peculiar to the w[?] and to the foetus.'

'Writers of Womens diseases' MsH 541.

A collection of drawings of the female reproductive system which may have been intended at one time to form part of his *Gyneciorum prodromus.*

DF78 24 drawings of the pudentia.
Artists, F. Boitard, P. L. Boitard, B.

DF79 Drawing on which the 2 figures illustrating James Douglas's paper, 'An account of a *hydrops ovarii'*, *Phil. Trans.* **xxv**, (1706) 2313, are based.
Artist, A(?).

DF80 In a folder made from a drawing of the *fundus uteri* and Fallopian tubes, and labelled by James Douglas, *'Uteri Icones'.*
17 drawings of the uterus.
3 copies of an engraving made from three of the drawings.
Artists, F. Boitard, B(?). Engraver unknown.

DF81 A list of figures 1-14, female reproductive system. Drawings in pen and wash that can be correlated with descriptions 3-8 inclusive and 10-13, plus a sketch for fig. 3 and an undescribed sketch stuck to fig. 4.
12 drawings. Artist, B(?).

DF82 2 different list of figures of female reproductive system. on a single sheet of paper.

i List of 19 *Tabulae*.
for which drawing for *Tabula* 8 can be identified.

ii List of 20 figures.
for which possible drawings for figures 2, 4, 5, 10 (2 drawings), 12, 15 (3 drawings), 17, 19, 20 (2 drawings) have been identified.

Two drawings dated 1711.
(Drawings for the other described *Tabulae* and figures probably in DF78, DF81 and DF85.)

In all, 13 sheets of drawings.
Artists, A(?), F Boitard.

A note by James Douglas on the variability of the blood vessels of the reproductive system.

DF83 Drawings of the pubic symphysis, of the attachment of the muscles of the pubic region to the pelvic girdle and of the relation of the vagina, distended during a birth, to the pelvic girdle.
5 pen and wash drawings.
Artists, F. Boitard, B.

DF84 Two pen and wash drawings of the placentas of twins.
Artist, B.

DF85 *'Figurae uteri foetusq humani'*.
12 March 1715. Rough list of figures of the reproductive system and of the foetus. - Descriptions of figures 5 and 6 have also numbers 8 and 9 against them in pencil.

DF86 'The explanation of some figures in which the organs of Generation in women, the parts peculiar to the foetus and the different postures wherein the child presents to the birth are accurately delineated as big as the life from whence they were taken accurate" J.D.

5 April 1715. .Full descriptions of 18 figures, rearranged from DF85.

24 pen and wash drawings that correspond with the descriptions. (There is uncertainty as to whether fig 3 ii has been correctly identified). Some of these have at some time been numbered in accordance with the descriptions.

DF87 A set of small copies of figs 1, 2, 4, 5, 8-11, 15, 17, 18 from DF86, one large-sized original and a small copy which is not described.

DF88 One large drawing which is similar in style to the rest of the drawings, but is not described.
Artists, F. Boitard, B.

DF89 'The dissection of the uterus in a woman six months after impregnation with the description of some of those parts peculiar to the human foetus. by J.D.' 12 Jan. 1715/16.

i. Dissecting notes and descriptions of figures made during the dissections between 2 and 4 January.

ii. A full description of 12 figures.

iii. 11 figures that correspond with the descriptions, all but the first numbered by James Douglas.

iv. A collection of 7 figures, 1-5 numbered by James Douglas, plus 2 which relate to the same subject which would provide material for figure 12.
Artist, B.

"Paper read by Dr Douglas concerning a description of the parts which are peculiar to a foetus in the womb" (JB, 26 Jan. 1715/16). This incorporated the material from this dissection.

Drawings from *post mortems* on pregnant women, with descriptions by James Douglas.

DF90 'The uterus, the labia and a hard substance from under the membrane of the coley *uteri* in a woman aged 40." 3 drawings.
Artist unknown.

DF91 An Explanation of the figures. Description of 7 figures.
Figs 1-4 of the ovary and clitoris "of a woman aged 38".
Fig. 5 "of a woman aged 35 that died the 4th day after delivery".
Figs 6 & 7, the pudentia of "a woman aged about 40".
Drawings 1, 2, 5 and 6 numbered by James Douglas. Drawing 3 has been used in DF86, Tab. 6, fig. 9.
Unnumbered drawing which may be figure 4.
Artist, F. Boitard.

DF92 Figure of the uterus of a "woman aged 31, ten weeks gone with child and died 6 days after miscarrying ..." 20 Oct. 1709.

DF93 Figures of two bony exfoliations separated from the *os pubes.*

DF94 2 rough drawings of the uterus, one showing the uterus opened, possibly by James Douglas, with notes by Douglas.

DF95 Drawing in pen and wash of uterus and vagina opened to show a growth at top of vagina.
Artist, F. Boitard.

DF96 3 drawings of diseased reproductive systems.

DF97 Description of fig. 9.
"fem: *an* 40 *nat:*of a glandulus wen at the top of the *fundus uteri.*"
This cannot be correlated with any figure.

DF98 Two records of the dimensions of the uterus, one dated 20 Aug. 1717.

DF99 A description of a *post mortem,* dated 27 Dec. 1704, (with transcription).

DF100 2 descriptions of *post mortem*, one dated 2 May 1717.

DF101 Miscellaneous figures in a grey folder, labelled possibly by James Douglas's son, Isaac James. 'Explanation of the Figures of the Uterus and Foetus'.
2 notes, one dated 15 Sept. 1711, on the blood supply to the reproductive system.
2 drawings by F. Boitard of small foetuses, one dated 26 July 1712 and labelled *'foetus mas 16 Septimanus a conceptu'.*

DF102 3 drawings, one of the Fallopian tube, ovary and round ligament, and two of the uterus pulled forward to uncover the rectum.
Artists, F. Boitard, B.

Between 1736 and 1740 Douglas had made a further number of drawings of the female reproductive system and the foetus, as if he again was working on *'Gyneciorum prodromus'.* Most of these drawings were done by James Parsons, who, during that period, was his anatomical assistant.

DF103 Drawings, some with preliminary sketches, of the uterus and placenta, by James Parsons. 13 items.

DF104 Drawings of diseased uteri, one with note attached by James Douglas, one with note by James Parsons. 14 drawings and 2 notes.

DF105 Sketches and finished drawings by James Parsons of foetuses, and three of the umbilical cord and its connections with the blood system of the foetus.

DF106 Drawing of monster, with note by James Parsons. Possibly the monstrous female foetus Parsons showed to the Royal Society on 24 Apr. 1737 (JB) and a sketch and drawings of monstrous heads, by James Parsons. 4 items.

DF107 6 drawings of *procidentia* by James Parsons.

DF108 Hermaphrodites.
One original drawing by James Parsons and 8

copies of plate made from it of the Angolan hermaphrodite. [BT D.3]
(See James Parsons, *A mechanical and critical enquiry into the nature of the hermaphrodite*, 1741).

One plate similar to the above, but containing also James Douglas's figures of the Charing Cross hermaphrodite, see DF60. This is the form of the plate used in James Parsons's work. Original drawing by James Parsons for Tab. I of this work.

DF109 'Abortuses'
3 drawings of abortuses by James Parsons with notes by James Douglas. One dated 23 Aug. 1738 and one dated 10 Sept. 1738.

DF110 'Miscellaneous figures'
1 drawing of a pregnant uterus.
1 drawings of uterus opened to show placenta.
1 drawing of a foetus partly removed from uterus.
3 drawings of an abortus.
All in red chalk.
Artist, C.

DF111 Male reproductive system.
4 black and white chalk drawings on grey paper, and 1 sketch in black chalk on white paper.
Artist P. R. Fremont.
1 sepia ink on white paper.
Artist, L. P. Boitard(?)
1 pencil drawing.
Artist unknown.
1 engraving by L.P.Boitard, that is similar in style to the pen drawing, but for which no original drawings exists.
6 fine red chalk drawings.
Artist, C.
1 description by James Douglas of a fig. 4 which cannot be identified.

Diaphragm and Thorax

James Douglas collected material on the diaphragm and thorax. No manuscripts relating to this subject exist. Some of the material could have been intended for Douglas's proposed 'Treatise of Aneurisms', a scheme for which is in D115.

DF112 An assemblage of engraved figures of the thorax from various sources, representing a history of illustration of the thorax.

i. From Thomas Geminus, *Compendiosa totuis anatomical delineatio,* (1553?).

ii. From Adriani Spigeli, *De humani corporis fabrica*, edition unknown, (c. 1627).

iii. From Carolus Stephanus, *De dissectione partium corporis humani,* French edition, (1546?).

iv. Missing.

v. From Ioannis Veslingii, *Syntagma anatomicum,* edition unknown, (c. 1650).

vi. From Philippe Verheyen, *Corporis humani anatomia.* Brussels (1710). Plate XVIII.

vii. From Philippe Verheyen, *Corporis humani anatomia,* Lovanii (1693).
Very similar to plate III.

viii. René Jacques Croissant de Garengeot. *Splanchnologie ou l'anatomie des Visceres,* (1728?).

ix. Caspari Bartholini, *Diaphragmatis,* edition not known. In the 1676 edition the figures that make up this plate are distributed in different plates.

x. *L'Anatomie d'Heister* (*Traduite du Latin par J. Senac*) (1724). This engraving has been cut from the copy of this book in the Hunterian Library. This copy was originally given by

Senac to John Freind, and must have come into James Douglas's possession possibly from the sale of John Freind's Library, 1729.

xi. Lorenzo Heister, *Compendium of Anatomy,* (1721).

xii. *Memoir de l'Acad.,* (1729) Plate XXIV, p. 186.

xiii. Albrecht von Haller *De musculis diaphragmatis dissertatio anatomica* (1733).

DF113 In a folder labelled by William Hunter. 'Drawings of the Diaphragma by JD'.

i. 3 pencils and wash drawings of the diaphragm and a proof plate of engravings of 2 of the drawings which were used to illustrate William Cheselden's *The anatomy of the humane body*, (1713), *Tab.* IX.
Artist, F. Boitard. Engraver, unknown.

ii. 2 pencil drawings of diaphragm.
Artist, unknown.

iii. Plan of the arrangement of 15 figures (no. 14 duplicated, though representing different figures, both of which are detached, no. 2 missing). None of the figures relates to the surviving drawings. [BT E. 13]

DF114 In a folder labelled by William Hunter. 'Drawings of the *Diaphragma* & contents of the thorax *in situ* by J.D.'
A set of 35 red chalk sketches of the diaphragm, thorax and heart, numbered, and the small sketches grouped together for the layout of *tabulae*.
Artist, James Parsons. [BT B2.3]

DF115 A set of finished red chalk drawings corresponding to the above sketches.
These have now been mounted according to the above plan and bound up (1976). Some of these drawings would cover Part 9 in Douglas's scheme for a 'Treatise of Aneurisms', D115, i.e. 'The course of the Aorta within the Thorax, in several

views, fairly exhibited'.
Artist, James Parsons.

DF116 25 sketches and finished red chalk drawings of the diaphragm, thorax and heart not included in the above collection. These also could cover Part 9 in the 'Treatise of Aneurisms'.
Artist, James Parsons.

DF117 4 engravings made from drawings in DF115 and DF116.
Engraver, unknown.

Other material relating to James Douglas's 'Treatise of Aneurisms', D115, for Part 6.

DF118 In a folder labelled by William Hunter, 'Aneurisms'.
"The anatomical Dissection of two internal aneurisms, one from a simple Dilatation of the Aorta; the other with a large Bagg of the same substance with the vessel itself; being both seated in the great arch on the curvature of the aorta Magna".
1 sketch and 5 finished drawings of aneurisms that could cover this part.
Artist, James Parsons.

DF119 In a folder labelled by William Hunter, 'Drawings & Designes of the parts concerned in VS'.
'Three figures representing the course of the veins, arteries and nerves in the bend of the elbow, together with a fair delineation of the Aponeurosis of the tendon of the Biceps muscle'.

i. 19 sketches and drawings of the blood system in the arm and hand, viewed from the surface and from dissection at various levels.
With plans and descriptions of the blood system by James Parsons.
Artist, James Parsons(?).

ii. 1 pencil drawing of the blood, muscle and nerve supply of the elbow.
Artist, unknown.

iii. 2 red chalk drawings, one of the surface blood vessels in the arm and the other of the elbow.
Artist, C.

DF120 3 sketches and 2 finished red chalk drawings of the blood supply and arrangement of muscles in the foot. These are similar in style to the drawings in DF119.
Artist, James Parsons(?).

Croonian Lectures

DF121 James Douglas was appointed to give the Croonian Lectures 1741-2. He gave the first lecture on the '*Membrana palati mobilis*. The uvula and *tuba Eustachinana* or canal of communication' on 18 March 1741/42 but died before giving the second lecture on the Bladder and the third on the windpipe and glottis. These were subjects in which Douglas had long been interested.

i. 2 sheets of drawings and a plate engraved from them of the trachea and associated structures, with a description by James Douglas that may refer to these drawings. These predate the proposed Croonian Lecture by many years.
Artist, F. Boitard.

ii. 3 black and white chalk drawings on grey paper.
5 red chalk drawings of the throat and associated structures.
Artists, P. R. Fremont(?), C, James Parsons(?).

iii. 1 red chalk drawing of the muscular coat of the bladder (human?).
Artist, C(?).

Post Mortems

DF122 'Gall bladder of woman aged 40'. 20 Oct. 1709.
Artist, A.

DF123 'Gall bladder with a large stone in its neck'. 5 July 1711.
Artist, F Boitard.

DF124 Two drawings, 28 July 1711.
'1) of the renal glands.
2) spleen of a girl aged 14 who dies with rotten bones'. [BT F 11, S 4]

DF125 'The explanation of some figures in which are fairly delineated the disposition of the muscles, nerves and blood vessels in a stump of an amputated thigh about five or six months after the operation was performed by J.D.' 30 Apr. 1717.
5 figures on 4 sheets, numbered by James Douglas, with descriptions.
Artist, B. [BT K.3]

DF126 In a folder made from a sheet of paper with bookplate(?) of the Duke of Newcastle(?), labelled by William Hunter, 'Drawings of Herniae' by J.D.

i. 'Hernia in a man of 34 years of age who had a fall from a horse'. 8 Apr. 1717.
Description of 4 figures and 4 drawings which may correspond with them.
Artist, B. [BT S2]

ii. '*Hydrops abdominis cum hernia Scroti*'
3 May 1717. An account of the case and descriptions of 3 figures. 4 drawings (one in duplicate). These have been numbered in pencil by the cataloguer to correspond with the figures. These have also been marked S. and J.D. in pencil by K Bryn Thomas.
Artist, B.

iii. 6 drawings of hernia without descriptions. Douglas may have planned to use this material on hernias for his advertised work.
Artist, B(?).

DF127 4 rough drawings of a "spleen of enormous bignes", 2 of the figures being on the recto and verso of one sheet, with notes added by James

Douglas and the weight added in French. And 2 rough drawings of the liver, probably from the same subject, with notes by James Douglas and the weight added in French.
An account of this case was read to the Royal Society by James Douglas, 22 Nov. 1711 (JB).

DF128 7 unidentified drawings.
Artist, various.

Miscellaneous anatomical drawings and prints

DF129 In a folder labelled by William Hunter, 'Designs of Blood vessels'.
7 drawings of parts of the blood system.
Artists, various.

DF130 5 drawings of the bladder *in situ* that may relate to either James Douglas's work on the peritoneum or his work on lithotomy.
Artists, various.

DF131 2 drawings and 2 copies of a plate made from them of the contents of the thorax and abdomen.
Artist, F. Boitard.

DF132 'What are the parts cut in the amputation of the leg 5 fingers below the knee'
In a folder made from a printed double sheet giving descriptions of figures of the eye in Latin and German.
Three sheets of figures and a description of one of the figures by James Douglas.
Artist, B(?).

DF133 In a folder labelled by William Hunter, 'Miscellaneous Drawings & Designs in Anatomy'.
6 drawings of unknown significance of various organs.
Artists, various.

DF134 In a folder labelled by James Douglas, 'Drawings forgot',
Description of 2 figures relating to James

Douglas's work on lithotomy, the figures are missing.

DF135 3 drawings of a skeleton, 2 of which are similar to Plate V, *Phil. Trans.* **xli** (1741), 810, which illustrates a letter from the Rt. Revd Father in God Robert, Lord Bishop of Corke, to the Rt. Hon. John Earl of Egmont, FRS, concerning an Extraordinary Skeleton. Additional letter p. 814.

Extracts of 2 letters from the Revd Dean Copping, FRS, to the President ... concerning the extra-ordinary Skeleton in the fore mentioned article, *Phil. Trans.* **xli** (1741) 814.

Part of a letter from Mrs - to Sir John Shadwell Kent MD ... concerning the extraordinary Skeleton mentioned in the two preceeding Papers.

The original, almost life-sized, drawings became the property of Sir Hans Sloane. But a remark on the back of one of these drawings, part of which is torn away:

"3 drawings J ...
from the Keal skele ...
ossifyed man Willia ...
In the County of Cor ...
Dr Barry ha ...
possession and h ...
In letting me ..."

suggests that these drawings also were original, taken from the skeleton and not reduced from the life-sized drawings.

DF136 *Vesica monstrosa D Isaaci Cansaboni 1 Julii a corpore exsecta AD 1614 Londini.*

DF136 'Cut of the urinary parts of William Phillips. The explication is at the end of the seventh history'.

DF138 Labelled by William Hunter, 'A monstrous Female child born near Aberdeen 1722'.

To Dr William Douglas, to be communicated to the Royal Society.
This transcribes an early labelling which has been partly trimmed away.
William Douglas, though not related to James Douglas, was a pupil of his in 1719, see W. Douglas, *A Second Letter to Dr Smellie,* London, ND, p 30.

DF139 Labelled by William Hunter, 'A set of Figures from Vesalius by some old Anatomist'.
36 plates from *Compendiosa totuis Anatomiae delineatio aere exarata per Thomas Geminum,* London (1559). [BT J. 11]

DF140 In a folder labelled by William Hunter, 'Miscellaneous Prints Anatomical etc.'
A number of prints from published works.

i. Figure from James Parsons, 'Some account of the *Phoea vitulus marinus* or sea-calf, shewed a Charing Cross in February 1742-3', *Phil. Trans.* **xlii** (1742), 383.

ii. Figure illustrating, 'An account of a Foetus that continued 46 years in the Mother's body' Communicated by Dr Steigerthal, *Phil. Trans.* **xxxi** (1721), 126.

iii. 2 plates illustrating, 'A letter from Dr James Parsons to Martin Folkes Esq., President of the Royal Society concerning the natural history of the Rhinoceros', *Phil. Trans.* **xlii** (1743) 523-541.

iv. 2 plates illustrating, 'Some account of the Insect called the Fresh Water Polypus by the President [Martin Folkes]', *Phil. Trans.* **xlii** (1742) 219.

v. Plate illustrating, 'Of Hydatides enclosed with a strong crust in the kidney of a sheep', by Mr W. Cowper, FRS, *Phil. Trans.* **xxv** (1706) 2304.

vi. Plate from Stephen Hales, *An account of some experiments and observations on Mrs Stephen's medicine for dissolving the stone*, London (1740).

vii. 2 plates illustrating Alexander Stuart's. Croonian lecture. Supplement to *Phil. Trans.* **xli** (1738) 615.

viii. 6 plates from Robert Nesbit, *Human osteogony explained in two lectures*, London (1736).

Robert Nesbit was brother-in-law to James Douglas, his wife being sister to James Douglas's wife. The book is dedicated to James Douglas.

ix, Plate published in an extended form, in *The Works of Alexander Monro, MD,* Edinburgh (1781).
Relating to the cure of a fractured *Tendo Achillis.*

DF141 2 plates from William Stukeley, *Of the spleen, its description and history ... to which is added some Anatomical Observation in the Dissection of an Elephant,* London (1723).

DF142 In a folder made from *Tab XI*, Cheselden's *Anatomy of the Humane Body*, London (1713), labelled, '*Icones Anatomici* D Cheselden'.

DF142.1 & .2 2 plates from Cheselden's *Anatomy of the Humane Body*, 2nd edn, 1722, based on original drawings made for James Douglas of the 'Hermaphrodite to be seen every day at Charing Cross'. 16 Feb. 1714/15.

DF142.3 & 4 2 plates from *Anatomy of the Humane Body,* 3rd edn, (1726).

DF142.5 1 plate from *The Anatomy of the Human Body,* 7th edn, (1778).

DF142.6 -.14 Plates from *Osteographia,* London, (1733).

DF142.15 -.21 Plates from 'Observations by Mr Cheselden' in *The Operations in Surgery of Mons. Le Dran*, London (1768).

DF142a 6 copies (1 duplicated) of Vesalius's figures from *De Fabrica,* (1543) by I. Wandelaar, and published in Andreae Vesalii, *Opera Omnia,* Hermanni and Bernhardi Siegfried Albini, 2 tomi, Lugduni Batavorum, (1725)

DF143 14 unidentified prints, some duplicated.

DF144 Duplicate plates of early 'Osteology'.

DF145 Proof plates and duplicates, 'Osteology' Part I.

DF146 Proof plates and duplicates, 'Osteology' Part II.

DF147 Duplicates of plates similar to those of Part II of the 'Osteology' but not included in it.

DF148 Proofs and duplicates of plates of the thorax.

DF149 Proofs and duplicates of plates of knee joint.

DF150 Proofs and duplicates of plates of muscular attachments.

DF151 Proofs and duplicates of plates of trachea.

DF152 Proofs and duplicates of reproductive system of hen.

DF153 Proofs and duplicates of plates from *Description of the Guernsey Lilly*, (1729).

After James Douglas's death, 9 of the figures made for James Douglas by F Boitard from Vesalius and Bidloo were assembled by his son, William George Douglas, and published as *Nine Anatomical Figures representing the External Parts, Muscles and Bones of the Human Body*, London (1748). A copy is in the Hunterian Library.

Douglas Figures

DF154 Duplicate of title page of *Nine Anatomical Figures*.

DF155 Duplicates of plates.

DOUGLAS RECORDS

The items listed in this section are a miscellaneous collection of correspondence relating to inquiries seeking additional information about the life of James Douglas and his various activities and interests. Inquiries as to possible Douglas archives in other institutions are also itemised. The listing includes microfilms of letters between Douglas and Patrick Blair, held in the Bodleian Library, Oxford, and of the Douglas Papers in the Library of the Royal Society, London.

Guernsey Lily

DR1 Correspondence relating to Alexander Marshall's painting of the Guernsey Lily, Royal Library, Windsor.

DR2 Letter in reply to enquiry if there was amongst the Duchess of Beaufort's flower picture, one of the Guernsey lily by Alexander Marshall that she might have removed from Marshall's '*Florileguim*' which she was lent by Robert Freind.

DR3 Correspondence over the Morins.
P. Morin was the first to describe and picture the Guernsey lily.

DR4 Correspondence over the classification of the Guernsey lily.

DR5 Correspondence over records of South African plants.

DR6 Correspondence relating to criticisms of James Douglas by Richard Bradley and John Martyn. For details of the latter, see R. Williamson, 'John Martyn and the Grub Street Journal', *Medical History* **v** (1961) 361-374, p.369.

DR7 Correspondence over D. Morand, owner of the copy of James Douglas's *Description of the Guernsey Lilly* (1729), now in the Bibliothèque Nationale, Paris.

DR8 Correspondence - in attempt to identify the sale in Brussels at which the Alexander Marshall flower paintings were sold, 1818.

DR9 Miscellaneous articles relating to Guernsey and the Guernsey lily.

DR10 Correspondence with Nerine Society.

DR11 Correspondence with Blanche Henrey, mainly over Thomas Knowlton, who was sent to Guernsey by James Douglas to enquire into the culture and history of the Guernsey lily in the island.

DR12 Correspondence with Rosemary De Sausmarez over editing James Douglas's *Description of the Guernsey Lilly*.

DR13 Correspondence over Thomas Knowlton's record of Yorkshire plants (see D447).

DR14 Correspondence over James Douglas's and James Parson's collection of figures of the rhinoceros. Hunterian Library Av 1.17 and At 1.15.

DR15 Correspondence over possible survival of James Douglas - B. S. Albinus correspondence.

DR16 Correspondence relating to visit to Paris, Sept. 1975, hoping to find evidence of James Douglas having studied in Paris.

DR17 Initial work on tracing the fate of James Douglas's collection of editions of the works of Horace.

DR18 Correspondence over James Douglas's grammatical works.

DR19 Correspondence over James Douglas's connection with St George's Hospital.

DR20 Correspondence over James Douglas's anatomical drawings.

DR21 Typescripts of papers relating to James Douglas.

DR22 Correspondence over Hertford garden at Enfield, mentioned by James Douglas in his *Description of the Guernsey Lilly*, 1729.

DR23 Miscellaneous correspondence enquiring for possible James Douglas records.

DR24 Correspondence over possible record of James Douglas - Sir David Hamilton connection.

DR25 Correspondence with David McClintock over James Douglas, the Guernsey lily, and the flora of Guernsey.

DR26 Correspondence with the Royal Archives, The Hague, relating to James Douglas's attendance on the Princess of Orange.

DR27 Correspondence over the Douglas drawings of the anatomy of the skate of which John Hunter gained possession.

DR28 Microfilm of 4^0 Rawlinson 323, Bodleian Library, Oxford, containing James Douglas - Patrick Blair letters.

DR29 Microfilm of Douglas Papers at the Royal Society.

i. A short account of the different kinds of ipecacuanha.

ii. Of the change of the Root in the Crocus autumnalis.
Read 25 Mar. 1725.

iii. Of the *Membrana Urinaria.*
Read 10 Feb. 1724

iv. An appendix to the anatomy of the bustard.

v. James Douglas's first Croonian Lecture on the *membrana palati mobilis*, uvula, and *Tuba Eustachi*, partly in Douglas's hand and partly in William Hunter's.

vi. A description of the human bladder.
James Douglas's Croonian Lecture, delivered

after his death by his son, William George, in William Hunter's handwriting.

vii. *Catalogus Universalis Pars Prima,* 24 Mar. 1726.

viii. A short description and demonstration of the parts belonging to the human eye that are affected by the *fistula lachrymalis*. 24 Dec. 1713.

ix. The description, virtues and use of a certain bark called in French *Du Chacril* and in Latin *Cortex Elatherii*. 8 Feb. 1721/2.

WILLIAM GEORGE DOUGLAS PAPERS

WGD1 Notes on surgery.
With occasional corrections by William Hunter.
pp 21.

WGD2 Notes taken at lectures, 11 Dec. 1741.
(?)Frank Nichols on anatomical preparations.
pp 4. [BT 25.4]

WGD3 A cure for dropsy. p 1.

WGD4 Anatomy notes. pp 3. [BT 25.5]

WGD5 Dissection notes. pp 8. [BT 6.2]

James Douglas had died before giving his second Croonian lecture on the bladder. William George, with William Hunter's help, put together some of his father's notes on the bladder into a paper and read it to the Royal Society.

WGD6 Draft of paper with additions and corrections by Hunter. pp 18.

The Royal Society holds a copy of the paper read to the Society, 27 May 1742, (L + P 1.100). The paper is in William Hunter's handwriting.

INDEX

All the catalogue entries for the Douglas papers begin with the letter D, to distinguish them from other groups of papers catalogued separately that originally formed the Blackburn Cabinet Papers, notably the Hunter papers and Clephane papers. To avoid unnecessary repetition in this index, the D is understood to apply throughout. Thus, numbers standing alone refer to D numbers in the catalogue and numbers prefixed with the letter F (for Figures) refer to DF numbers in the catalogue.

In the Index, where reference is made to material which has no catalogue number (eg introductory text or cross references) then the numbers of the proceeding entry is given in italics.